# Structural steel design to BS 5950: Part 1

# Structural steel design to BS 5950: Part 1

Frixos Joannides and Alan Weller

Thomas Telford

Published by Thomas Telford Publishing, Thomas Telford Ltd,
1 Heron Quay, London E14 4JD. URL: http://www.thomastelford.com

Distributors for Thomas Telford books are
*USA*: ASCE Press, 1801 Alexander Bell Drive, Reston, VA 20191–4400, USA
*Japan*: Maruzen Co. Ltd, Book Department, 3–10 Nihonbashi 2-chome, Chuo-ku, Tokyo 103
*Australia*: DA Books and Journals, 648 Whitehorse Road, Mitcham 3132, Victoria

First published 2002

**Also available from Thomas Telford Books**

*Structural detailing in steel*. M Y H Bangash. ISBN 07277 2850 4
*Steel space frames*. G S Ramaswamy, M Eakhout and G R Suresh. ISBN 07277 3014 2

A catalogue record for this book is available from the British Library

ISBN: 0 7277 3012 6

This book is published on the understanding that the author is solely responsible for the statements made and opinions expressed in it and that its publication does not necessarily imply that such statements and/or opinions are or reflect the views or opinions of the publishers. While every effort has been made to ensure that the statements made and the opinions expressed in this publication provide a safe and accurate guide, no liability or responsibility can be accepted in this respect by the editor(s)/author(s) or publishers.

Typeset and designed by Bookcraft Ltd, Stroud, Gloucestershire.
Printed and bound in Great Britain by MPG, Bodmin, Cornwall.

# Contents

## Acknowledgements

Grateful acknowledgement by the authors is made to all the friends and acquaintances both in Ireland and the United Kingdom, who contributed to the development of this book.

The authors also express their thanks to BSI, University College Dublin and Parthenon Press for their kind permission to reproduce material from their publications.

## Accuracy of calculations

The advent of calculators and computers has tended to give the impression that calculations may be carried out to a very high degree of accuracy and that we know exactly how a structure behaves. This is a complete mistake, compounded by the term 'more exact method' used in the last revision of BS 5950: Part 1. The reader must remember that the loading on a structure is only an approximation, at best, and that before any other tolerances are considered there is a 2.5% rolling tolerance on the material. Many structures built until about 1980 were designed using a slide rule, which limited the accuracy of any calculations, and have shown no deficiencies. In preparing this book, the authors have tried to indicate the type of accuracy which is sufficient for practical structural calculations. Section properties taken from the latest publications may vary very slightly, due to the rounding errors in calculation and the assumptions made in the calculations. The authors have used the latest section properties taken from BS 4: Part 1: 1993 and BS EN 10056: 1999. Any slight variation in numbers will have no real impact on the final structure and may, generally, be ignored in practice.

## Units

Metric units do not lend themselves to sensible numbers, as may be seen in the section tables, where the dimensions are given in mm and the derived properties in cm units. As engineers we have to try and avoid errors in calculations. The clear presentation of arithmetic is a great help in this and the authors have adopted, as far as possible, a policy of using the section sizes and properties as given in the tables. In addition, spans have been given in metres and moments in kNm. The appropriate power of 10 has been inserted in the expressions to ensure the agreement of the numbers and units that have been used in all cases. All designers are advised to adopt a similar system to prevent possible errors, as a slip to the power 10 is well outside the mistakes covered by any normal factor of safety.

# Preface

Structural Eurocodes will eventually replace national codes like BS 5950. However, this situation will be reached in some years time. Therefore the BSI committee responsible for BS 5950 decided in 1997 to amend the technical content of that document, based on changes which have been highlighted by the preparation of the Eurocode. It was also felt that some rewording would improve the clarity and avoid conflicting interpretations. In addition, the standards, referred to in BS 5950, for materials and loading, have been modified for various reasons and cross-referencing needed correction.

This book, an update of *Structural Steelwork (Elementary Design to BS 5950)*, has been produced to comply with the limit states code *BS 5950 – 1:2000 (incorporating Corrigendum No. 1) Structural use of Steelwork in building, Part 1: Code of practice for design – rolled and welded sections*.

This book is intended as an elementary course in structural steelwork for students of civil or structural engineering. It is also hoped that it will be a help to those engineers who have had little experience of structural steelwork and wish to improve their grasp of the topic, without being daunted by too much detail. Great care has been taken in the technical exposition and practical illustrations of the material presented. Theory is immediately followed by worked examples for the sake of better and clearer understanding.

With this book the authors hope to provide a short integrated course which students commencing the study of steel design will find stimulating and useful.

August 2001

# 1. Introduction

## 1.1. History

Iron first came into use as a structural material when the cast-iron bridge, an arch of 100 ft (30.4 m) span, was built by A Darby in 1779 over the River Severn, near Coalbrookdale in England. Wrought iron, with a much higher tensile strength, followed, being the first real stage in the introduction of steel.

Up to about 1890, wrought iron formed the main material for iron buildings and bridges, being often used in combination with cast iron. The engineering achievements of that time are really remarkable.

Mild steel dates back to 1856 when Henry Bessemer introduced his steel-making process which reduced the cost of steel considerably. In 1865, Siemens and Martin invented the open-hearth process, named after them, and this was used extensively for structural steel production. However, it was not until 1879 that clean, high-quality steel could be produced in bulk. In that year, Gilchrist and Thomas introduced the basic lining into the Bessemer converter and open-hearth furnace. This lining, made of magnasite or lignasite, had the effect of removing phosphorus. The result was that low-phosphorous steel could be produced from local high-phosphorous iron ores.

The major method of producing steel nowadays is the basic oxygen process, where steel scrap and molten iron are fed into a vessel and oxygen is blown through. In this method, the liquid metal from the blast furnace is transferred to a 250 tonne solid bottom vessel together with a proportion of scrap to act as a coolant. When the vessel is loaded, a water-cooled oxygen lance is lowered and compressed commercial oxygen is forced in. After twenty minutes, the whole charge in the vessel becomes pure iron. This is then alloyed into a ladle to the correct composition.

Modern steels are cast using the continuous casting process, sometimes known as the concast method. In this, the liquid steel from the basic oxygen process is poured into the top of a mould and then taken out of the bottom as a continuous ribbon of steel. When this is sufficiently cooled, it is cut into billets for further processing.

The advantage of this system is that large quantities of high-grade steel can be produced in a single works with the minimum of labour; however, with this system small quantities of non-standard steel cannot be produced.

## 1.2. Types of steel

Most countries have their own steel specifications. In this book, only the types used in Europe will be considered; these are, in fact, similar to those used throughout the world.

Steel is now supplied to the European standards, which are BS EN 10025, for bulk steels used in construction, and BS EN 10113, for fine grain steels. Sometimes, other steels are also used. The versions of the standards issued by BSI for use in the UK are prefaced BS and are published in English.

These standards now replace BS 4360 and the other British Standards used previously.

The mass of steel is calculated on the basis that the steel has a density of 7 850 kg/m$^3$.

## 1.3. Structural design

For a structural design to be satisfactory, generally four major objectives must be fulfilled. These are:

- Utility or function (strength and serviceability)
- Safety (permanence)
- Economy
- Elegance

### 1.3.1. Utility or function

The structure must fulfil its intended function. This function may be complex, concerned with the support of the load, with thermal and sound insulation, with watertightness and fire resistance. The load itself may be complex; it may be a wide spectrum of loads or it may be a combination of different loads.

Moreover, as soon as a structure is built, various causes of deterioration commence to act upon it, e.g. the influence of the weather, ill use, accident and fatigue.

The designer must not only make sure that his structure will not fall down, but he must also see that his structure should not develop serious cracks or unsightly deflections, or vibrate alarmingly due to wind or other actions or sink excessively into the ground. In other words, the structure must have strength and serviceability during its intended life.

### 1.3.2. Safety

The structure must be safe and have a sufficient degree of permanence during its intended life. Many structures involve the public and the consequences of collapse must be made remote.

### 1.3.3. Economy

The client having decided, doubtless in consultation with his designer, on the standard of strength, durability and other qualities he requires, entrusts his designer to look for the best value for his money. Design decisions are often economic decisions because nearly all structures are built with some limit of expenditure in mind and this financial constraint has an important bearing on the influence of the other objectives. In particular, the initial cost may not be the only consideration; the client should be persuaded to look at the long-term use of the structure and the possibility of accommodating future changes. However, reasonable economy is a requirement for a good structure, but economy should not be carried to excess; reasonable economy is not the same thing as meanness.

### 1.3.4. Elegance

The structure should be elegant and a joy to whoever looks at it. By this we do not mean a structure filled with senseless embellishment, but just simply having a good functional appearance.

The designer with a feeling for good appearance knows how to modify purely structural elements to give them visual beauty.

It is interesting to look at these four requirements from a historical point of view.

The barbaric age required only strength and function.

The next age, when people became socially conscious, required safety and permanence along with strength and function.

When the commercial age was reached, economy became very prominent and it was added to the requirements of a good structure.

Finally, when civilisation advanced further, elegance was inserted.

## 1.4. Design

The word design has many connotations. One may accept as structural design everything from the initial conception to the final plans and specifications. This involves all the phases of a structural project, so let us consider the following list of phases in detail:

A  Initial planning
B  Preliminary design
C  Final design
    a. Analysis
    b. Selection and proportioning of elements
    c. Drawings, specifications and other contract document
D  Invitation and acceptance of tender
E  Construction
F  Operation and maintenance

### 1.4.1. Initial planning

Initial planning starts with the requirements of the structure. It may include a feasibility study, in which the project is considered within the limits of practicability.

During this phase, the engineer acts as a consultant to the prospective owner, architect, builder or financier. He must be capable not only of recognising the more-or-less standard structural systems, which are worthy of investigation in the particular case, but also devising new or modified systems to meet the particular requirements. Also, the engineer should pay attention to the aesthetic value of a structure. In many cases, the requirements of good appearance can be met without excessive cost.

At this stage, very rough designs are made with only a few computations, reliance being placed chiefly on judgement and experience. The approximate costs of promising schemes are estimated and compared, and tentative budgets and time schedules are prepared. If a site has not been predetermined, the engineer may be involved with site selection as well.

There are also other considerations, including legal, financial and sociological aspects with which the engineer may find himself involved.

So, it is clear that this stage of design calls for an engineer of experience, skill, general knowledge and imagination.

It is also clear that the ideas generated and the course set in the early work may control the success or failure of the entire project.

### 1.4.2. Preliminary design stage

Having passed the test of feasibility, the project enters the preliminary design phase. Here, the first rough designs are reviewed and partially refined. In many cases, the general layout of a structure is selected from many possible alternatives. Sometimes, differences are not clear-cut, and it is necessary to carry more than one scheme to final design or even to the point of competitive tender.

This phase of design usually finalises the choice of structural type and the choice of material, if these have not already been selected in the initial planning stage, and also establishes the main dimensions of the structure and the location of the principal members.

Refinement, alterations and corrections are made throughout the final design phase.

### 1.4.3. Final design stage

Before a refined and detailed structural analysis can be carried out, it is necessary to make a final determination of the loads for which the structure is to be designed, including both loads determined from codes of practice and the self-weight of the structure. However, it is part of the designer's responsibility to specify the load conditions and to take care of exceptional cases.

Once the basic form of the structure and the external loads are defined, structural analyses are made to determine the internal forces in various members of the structure and size of each member.

In the proportioning of elements, the engineer must keep in mind the criteria of adequate strength and rigidity, ease of connection, fabrication and erection, economy and maintenance.

The preparation of contract drawings, job specifications and other contract documents may also be included as part of the final design. They are generally prepared under the supervision of the structural engineer or with his assistance.

### 1.4.4. Invitation and acceptance of tender

In the fourth phase, the structural engineer usually assists in the invitation of tenders and may take part in negotiations with the prospective contractors. Frequently, contractors raise technical questions or propose design alternatives requiring his judgement. Finally, the engineer may be involved in the review of competitive bids and, after thorough consideration, he recommends the selection of the one which appears to be the most favourable for the project under consideration.

### 1.4.5. Construction

During the fifth phase, the detailed shop drawings of the steel fabricator and other manufacturers are submitted to the engineer for approval.

Generally when construction starts, a representative of the engineer remains in residence on the site, or, on a small project, visits it periodically.

The primary duties of the resident engineer are as follows:

- to ensure that the materials and workmanship comply with the speci-fications
- to check the line and level of the structure, and
- to see that the drawings are followed.

He is also concerned with project scheduling and progress.

In addition, he may be asked to issue instructions for remedying possible faults in the structure and to redesign part of the work to the extent that it is delegated to him by the structural engineering consultant.

### 1.4.6. Operation and maintenance

Once the job is completed, operation and maintenance pass to other hands. However, new construction frequently goes through a period during which minor alterations are found necessary. This is particularly true in novel structures or those incorporating some innovation in detail. During this period, the engineer remains intimately involved in the project.

## 1.5. Further considerations

Several points in the above breakdown require additional comment.

In practice, the dividing lines between phases may not be distinct. Different phases may be combined or dispensed with. For instance, the practicability of a project may be so obvious that a feasibility study is unnecessary. In other cases, the choice of structural system is so clear that final design can begin almost immediately.

However, the search for the best solution, which follows the initial creative impulse, is a repetitive operation. Ideas, methods of analysis and member sizes or arrangements are proposed and tested, sometimes rejected, sometimes modified and frequently refined in the course of arriving at the final solution.

The final solution is a satisfactory balance among various factors; material selection, economics, client desires, financial ability and various architectural considerations. Seldom, except possibly in the most elementary structure, will a unique solution be obtained – unique in the sense that two structural engineering firms would obtain exactly the same solution.

In the past and still at present, this procedure is largely intuitive. In recent years, some techniques for systematising and generally assisting the design process have emerged. For example, the calculative powers of digital computers enable the consideration of more alternatives for a given situation.

The range and applicability of these techniques are certain to expand. But while they will permit increased sophistication in design, it is doubtful that they will ever eliminate the need for individual creativity and high-level professional competence in engineering technology.

**Note**: The pronoun *she* is equally applicable whenever the pronoun *he* is used in the text.

# 2. Elasticity

## 2.1. Behaviour of structural materials under load

All solid materials deform under load. Until a critical load is reached the deformation is elastic, i.e. the structure returns to its original shape when the load is removed. The critical load on a unit of cross-section is known as the elastic limit. If materials have low elastic limits then they do not constitute suitable structural materials. Figure 2.1 shows typical load/deformation diagrams for concrete and steel.

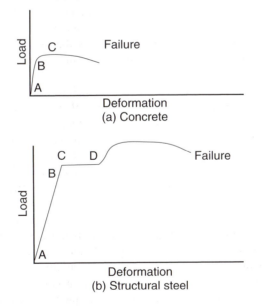

Fig. 2.1.

AB = elastic range
C = yield point
CD = plastic stage, when strain increases without increase in stress

Deformation is an essential condition for structural equilibrium since internal forces in the material must resist the loads imposed on the materials. So long as the material remains a single entity then it may carry a load. However, if there is a fracture then failure takes place. Structural steel is capable of carrying large loads even with deformation and is, therefore, a ductile material.

Among the other major structural materials, concrete is typically brittle and aluminium is typically ductile under normal circumstances.

Most brittle materials fail much more easily in tension than in compression, because once a crack develops it spreads quickly in tension; however, a far larger force is required to cause a compression failure. Concrete, the most important brittle material, has a compressive strength many times its tensile strength. One way of overcoming the weakness of concrete in tension is the provision of steel reinforcing bars.

In ductile materials, the tensile strength is about the same as the compressive strength.

The elastic deformation of every structural material is directly proportional to the load it carries. This proportionality of load to deformation was first recorded by Robert Hooke in 1678.

Hooke's law, which forms the basis of elastic design, may then be expressed as stress proportional to strain:

$$f \propto e$$

$$\text{or } f = E.e \tag{2.1}$$

where:

$f$ = stress

$e$ = strain

$E$ = a constant, which is called the *modulus of elasticity* or *Young's modulus*.

The *modulus of elasticity*, or *Young's modulus*, varies from material to material, but it is a constant for each material.

Stress can therefore be thought of as strain multiplied by the constant $E$.

The units of $E$ are the same as for stress, since strain is a pure number, a ratio of length to length. The value of $E$ for S 275 steel (Mild Steel) is about 205 000 N/mm$^2$.

In order to relate the strength of steel to that of the material, the Standards for the material give values for the minimum yield strength ($p_y$) and ultimate strength; it should be noted that the yield strength is normally taken as the design strength. These values are obtained by testing particular grades of material and noting the minimum values, which may be obtained reliably in testing. These values are then used for all design purposes.

The following typical values are normally employed (see also Table 9 of BS 5950):

| Steel grade | Thickness less than or equal to mm | Design strength $p_y$ N/mm$^2$ |
|---|---|---|
| S 275 | 16 | 275 |
| | 40 | 265 |
| | 63 | 255 |
| | 80 | 245 |
| | 100 | 235 |
| | 150 | 225 |
| S 355 | 16 | 355 |
| | 40 | 345 |
| | 63 | 335 |
| | 80 | 325 |
| | 100 | 315 |
| | 150 | 295 |

## 2.2. Tension test of steel

When choosing a material, it is essential to know its properties and its ability to withstand stress. The various mechanical properties of a material are determined by laboratory tests and, in the case of steel, the supply standards require, among other things, that the manufacturer shall carry out tension tests on specimens taken from each type of section rolled from each cast of steel, in order to verify that the material has the specified mechanical properties.

To perform a laboratory tension test, a piece of material is cut from the parent material and turned into a cylindrical test specimen, such as that shown in Fig. 2.2(a). After marking the gauge length on the specimen, by making two small indentations, it is placed in the testing machine. This exerts a tensile force on the specimen, which may be measured at any time during the test. An extensometer, which is an instrument for accurately measuring changes in length, is attached to the specimen. Then a slowly increasing tensile load is applied to the specimen until fracture occurs.

At first the specimen stretches so little that the extension cannot be visibly detected. At this stage, if the load is removed, the test piece will return to its original length, thus demonstrating the elasticity of the steel.

When the load is further increased, a point is reached at which extension can be noticed visibly and extension ceases to be proportional to the load.

This is known as the yield point, and at this stage the steel specimen continues to extend for a time without an increase in load. After this extension, during which the material behaves plastically, the steel recovers some of its resistance to stretching, because of strain hardening, and it is necessary to increase the load, if the test is to be continued. However, the steel has been considerably weakened due to the reduction of cross-sectional area and stretches more for each increment of load.

In the final stage, the test piece becomes a little thinner at one part before eventually breaking at this neck or waist. In actual fact, just before fracture, the load can be decreased because the cross-section at which the break occurs becomes considerably reduced.

At intervals during the test, measurements of load and elongation are made and the behaviour of the specimen during the test is usually expressed graphically by plotting stress (load per unit area) against strain (extension per unit length).

The graph for a Grade S 275 steel, or mild steel specimen, which shows certain characteristics more clearly than higher strength steels, is shown in Fig. 2.2(b). It is worth noting that the modern steels produced by continuous casting show a less well-defined shape than that demonstrated in Fig. 2.2; this will have little effect on design procedures.

The stress at point E is known as the tensile strength of the steel. It is the ratio of maximum load achieved during the test over the gross cross-sectional area of the specimen.

Figures for minimum yield stress or strength in BS EN 10025, for grade S 275 steels, are shown in BS 5950 Table 9.

The slope of the straight line portion of the stress–strain diagram, i.e. the ratio of stress to strain, is known as the modulus of elasticity or Young's modulus, called after Dr Thomas Young who, in 1807, was the first to suggest the ratio of stress to strain to measure the stiffness of a material.

As was observed during the tension test, when a bar lengthens as a result of tension, its diameter reduces. Thus experimentation has shown that an axial elongation is always accompanied by a lateral contraction, and for a given material strained within its elastic region, the ratio of lateral strain to axial strain is a constant, known as *Poisson's ratio*, called after SD Poisson, a French mathematician, who formulated this concept in 1828.

$$\frac{\text{lateral strain}}{\text{axial strain}} = \text{Poisson's ratio}$$

For most metals, Poisson's ratio lies between $\frac{1}{4}$ and $\frac{1}{3}$; BS 5950 gives a value of 0.3 for steel.

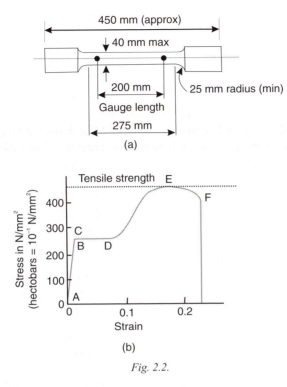

*Fig. 2.2.*

AB = elastic range
C = yield point
CD = plastic stage, when strain increases without increase in stress
DEF = behaviour after strain hardening occurs
F = failure (breaking) point

## 2.3. Brittle fracture

Brittle fracture is the sudden failure of the material under service conditions, caused by low temperature or sudden changes in stress. Thick material is more prone to this phenomenon than thin, resulting in many of the rules governing the design against the risk of brittle fracture being based on a limiting thickness. It will also be found that the stress in the material and type of details employed in the construction will have a very significant effect on the risk of brittle fracture occurring.

BS 5950: Part 1 has a factor ( BS 5950 Table 3) depending on the detail and stress in the material; when there is compression this has a high value allowing greater thickness; when there is tension this is reduced, depending on the level of tension. When the tension exceeds 0.3 of the nominal yield strength (i.e. that of material less than 16 mm thick) then the factor has its lowest value.

The detail governs the type of surface of the material; when there is a smooth surface with no working then the value is high; if, however, there are imperfections on the surface from welding and cutting, then the value is low.

The method of determining the maximum thickness of material against the possibility of brittle fracture given in the code is as follows:

- Determine the minimum temperature of the steel during the life of the structure; this will normally be –5 °C for internal frames, or –15 °C for those exposed to the elements. Figures have now also been included for structures subject to lower temperatures.
- Determine the thickness of steel being employed.
- Determine the value of $K$ for the most critical detail from Table 3 of BS 5950.
- Divide the thickness by the value of $K$.
- Depending on the type of material, whether sections or flats or hollow sections, look up the grade of steel in either BS 5950 Table 4 or Table 5 for the thickness and lowest temperature.

Note that material thicker than the maximum value given in BS 5950 Table 6 may not be used without further investigation, as this is the maximum normally tested.

In the event that the conditions given in the simple steps and tables are not met then the engineer is also given a number of equations to enable him to determine the risk of brittle fracture in the particular circumstances of his design.

*Example 2.3.1. A plain beam, of grade S 275 steel, is in an exposed situation outside a building where the design temperature is –25 °C. The flange thickness is 36.6 mm and the section is fully stressed in bending. Find the minimum grade of steel for this section. If holes are punched unreamed in the compression flange what will be the effect? What will be the effect of punching unreamed holes in the tension flange?*

## SOLUTION

From Table 3 in BS 5950, a fully-stressed, plain steel section in tension gives a value for the factor $K$ of 2.

This means that the minimum thickness required when consulting Table 4 is $36.6/2 = 18.3$ mm.

The minimum quality to satisfy the conditions is J0, which can be used up to a basic thickness of 30 mm at –25 °C.

Using the equation $t = Kt_1$, the maximum flange thickness for a section in this location is $2 \times 30 = 60$ mm.

If holes are punched in the compression flange then the value of $K$ remains at 2 and the same quality of steel is acceptable.

If, however, the holes are punched in the tension flange then the value of $K$ changes to 1; so the limiting thickness must be taken as the actual thickness, 30 mm, from BS 5950 Table 3.

In order to satisfy the requirements, the steel must be Grade J2, which may be used up to a thickness of 65 mm.

Looking at BS 5950 Table 4, it should be noted that the presence of welding provides severe limitations on the thickness of material which may be freely used if there is a risk of brittle fracture.

## 2.4. Fatigue

Fatigue takes place when a member or connection is subject to repeated stress variations, even if these are small. In building structures, BS 5950 requires fatigue to be considered only if there is the possibility of a significant number of variations in stress. The commonest is in cranes where their classification is U4 to U9, in BS 2573, or where there is a high risk of wind-induced oscillations.

In the event that a fatigue check is required, BS 5950 refers to BS 7608.

# 3. Factor of safety

## 3.1. Types of limit states

As was noted in the tension test of the steel specimen, there is a definite point called the yield point, at which steel begins to yield or flow to an appreciable extent. Consequently, if a structure is stressed to yield point, major deformation may commence. It is, therefore, clear that structures must be designed in such a way that the actual stress never exceeds this yield point.

This differentiation between failure of the test specimen and failure of structure is important and must be clearly understood.

When considering limit states behaviour, it is usual to assume that failure has occurred when the yield stress has been attained across the section. The reason for this is that once yield stress has been reached the deformations make the structure unacceptable.

The introduction of limit states as a design philosophy has altered the thinking in the new codes of practice for most materials. The essential features of limit states design are the considerations when the structure becomes unsuitable for its use. Two main divisions of limit states are recognised:

- The ultimate limit state which can be considered as the failure of the structure.
- The serviceability limit state where, although capable of carrying the imposed loads, the response makes the structure unfit for its intended purpose.

BS 5950 (Table 1) has designated the individual states as:

| Ultimate limit state | Serviceability limit state |
|---|---|
| Strength (including general yielding, rupture, buckling and forming a mechanism) | Deflection |
| Stability against overturning and sway stability | Vibration |
| Fracture due to fatigue | Wind-induced oscillation |
| Brittle fracture | Corrosion |

Each of these limit states will now be considered in turn.

### Strength

It is required of all structures that they are capable of carrying the loads imposed upon them. Failure may take a number of forms:

- Axial compression, where the material will be shortened or where the whole section may buckle.
- Bending, forming plasticity and high deformations of the member in question.
- Axial tension, causing significant elongation or fracture of the material.
- Shear, causing failure of the web or a panel with diagonal distortion.
- Local buckling, which will affect compression and shear, reducing the capacity below that which would be expected from the application of simple theory to the members as a whole. This mode of failure will predominate in cold-formed sections in particular, although some of the thinner, hot-finished plates and sections will also be affected.

It is these modes of failure which will form the primary mode for design.

### Stability

Not only must the structural members support their loads but also the structure as a whole must be stable against overturning or uplift. This stability must be considered using factored loads and restraining forces. In particular it should be noted that low factors are applied to those forces which provide restraint to guard against them being overestimated.

In addition to overturning and uplift, the structure must also be insensitive to sway; in other words there must not be excessive lateral deformation under vertical loads (see Fig. 3.1).

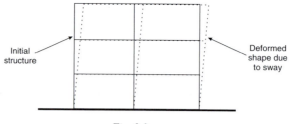

Fig. 3.1.

The simplest way given in the code to check for sway is to apply a notional lateral force to the structure based on the vertical load at each level. This lateral force is taken as 0.5 per cent of the sum of the factored dead and imposed loads (see Fig. 3.2). These lateral forces are intended to ensure that the structure has sufficient internal resistance to lateral loads and imperfections to keep its shape. They should not be applied to the design of foundations or included in other lateral loads.

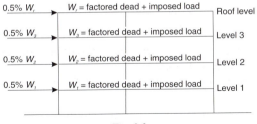

| | | |
|---|---|---|
| 0.5% $W_r$ | $W_r$ = factored dead + imposed load | Roof level |
| 0.5% $W_3$ | $W_3$ = factored dead + imposed load | Level 3 |
| 0.5% $W_2$ | $W_2$ = factored dead + imposed load | Level 2 |
| 0.5% $W_1$ | $W_1$ = factored dead + imposed load | Level 1 |

*Fig. 3.2.*

These forces are alternatives to the wind force and other horizontal forces, which must also be applied to the structure and must not be less than 1.0 per cent of the factored dead load. This wind force must be applied to all sections of a structure, even if they are internal and not subject to applied wind.

As well as the requirement for sway due to structural imperfections and applied lateral loads, $P - \Delta$ effects may reduce the strength of the structure. These are shown in Fig. 3.3(a), where a simple column A–$\Gamma$ carries an axial compressive load, $P$. In the perfect situation this column would fail at the Euler load, but due to the imperfections in the material, and unintentional eccentricity of loading, it will move out of plane well before this load is reached. This then results in a situation where the column starts to sway at a relatively low load, giving a moment equal to $P$–$\Delta$ in addition to the compressive force. This is clearly going to reduce the capacity of the section to carry the applied load $P$. In the same way in a frame, the effects of applying a vertical load can cause the frame to sway with a loss in overall capacity (see Fig. 3.3(b)).

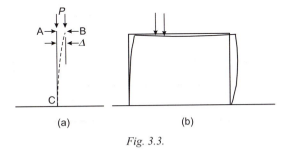

(a)                    (b)

*Fig. 3.3.*

The code covers this in §2.4.2 by requiring the engineer always to check for sway stability by determining the value of $\lambda_{cr}$, the critical load factor, that the structure can sustain. In order to do this, the factored applied loads, as shown in Fig. 3.2, are applied to the structure and a linear elastic analysis is carried out to determine the horizontal deflections. From this, the smallest value of $\lambda_{cr}$ is determined using the expression:

$$\lambda_{cr} = \frac{h}{200\delta}$$

where:

> $h$ is the storey height
> $\delta$ is the difference in horizontal deflection between the top and bottom of the storey

The check is carried out on each storey in turn in order to determine the lowest value.

If $\lambda_{cr}$ is equal to or greater than 10 then the structure is not sensitive to sway and no further action is required. If the value of $\lambda_{cr}$ is less than 10 then the structure is sway sensitive and must be checked using the rules given in §2.4.2.7. If $\lambda_{cr}$ is less than 4.0 then either the frame must be stiffened, by the addition of bracing, or a second order analysis must be carried out to prove the suitability of the frame. It will be found that structures with very low values of $\lambda_{cr}$ are likely to be rejected because they will have high deflections under loading, especially that of wind or other lateral forces.

## Fatigue

In structures subjected to frequent change of stress, failure may occur at stress levels well below normal yield. This phenomenon is not common in most building structures, although in such cases as gantries and platforms carrying vibrating machinery, the possibility must be considered. Fatigue checks are carried out at working loads considering the stress variations, which occur, in the normal working cycle.

## Brittle Fracture

As with fatigue, brittle fracture will occur only rarely in building construction. Before a brittle fracture failure can occur a combination of tensile stress, low temperature, thick material and rapid change of stress must be present. The usual measure of steel ductility used to assess liability to failure is the Charpy impact test. Each grade of steel has a specified minimum value of impact energy at a given temperature (normally 27 joules). Details of the design rules are described in Chapter 2.

## Deflection

The maximum deflection, calculated by the engineer, is dependent on circumstances. Deflections affecting the strength and stability of the structure are controlled by the rules for the ultimate states. The main concern of deflection as a serviceability state is that the structural response to loading is such that the user accepts that there is no cause for anxiety. This type of behaviour may be typified by sagging appearance, plaster cracking or failure to align plant and machinery. The design engineer must assess each case on its merits, although some guidance has been provided in codes of practice.

*Vibration*

With the development of lighter structures there is a higher risk of vibration becoming critical in a number of situations. In general, most building frames will not be unduly sensitive to vibration in normal use; however, particular care must be exercised when vibrating loads are applied to the structure. Some particular cases include plant platforms, cranes and situations where such activities as dancing, marching and drilling occur. In these situations, care must be taken to ensure that the structural response will not amplify the disturbing motion. The method of correction when this happens is to change the natural frequency of the structure. Changing the load factor will not necessarily cure the problem.

*Corrosion*

Generally, corrosion of steel will be critical only when it is exposed to moisture, oxygen and, possibly, pollutant materials in the atmosphere. Painting is the normal method of protection used to prevent this. A number of paint systems can be applied, each having its own advantages. In order to ensure a firm base for the protective coat, the steel is frequently first prepared by subjecting it to blast cleaning to remove any loose material and rust.

The process leaves the surface clean and slightly rough enabling a good base to be formed. The level of protection provided by a modest paint system will ensure that the steel will have a long life in a normal, dry building situation. Here much of the paintwork is cosmetic rather than protective. For steel in external or aggressive internal situations a higher standard of protection is required; full details of protective systems are given in BS 5493 and in various guides produced by the steel industry.

## 3.2. Factors of safety

Design implies that we will have a structure with an adequate factor of safety against failure taking into account the various facets, which affect safety levels. These include:

- The assumptions and processes used in design.
- The details prepared by the drawing office.
- The various processes in making the steel plates and sections and the resultant material properties.
- The work carried out on the material during fabrication and erection.
- The tolerances in the material during fabrication and erection.
- The material strength variation.

Clearly the engineer will not have the time to assess these factors in detail for each project. The codes have, therefore, been prepared using experience to enable rational values to be used. Because statistical values are not available to cover every aspect of each variable, experience and judgement are used to derive the values, which can be employed for everyday design. It is these values which have been incorporated into codes of practice for structural steel design. In BS 5950 the following tables give the values that have been adopted:

BS 5950 Table 2. Partial factors for loads $\gamma_f$.

| Loading | Factor $\gamma_f$ |
|---|---|
| Dead load, except as follows. | 1.4 |
| Dead load acting together with wind load and imposed load combined. | 1.2 |
| Dead load acting together with crane loads and imposed load combined. | 1.2 |
| Dead load acting together with crane loads and wind load combined. | 1.2 |
| Dead load whenever it counteracts the effects of other loads. | 1.0 |
| Dead load when restraining sliding, overturning or uplift. | 1.0 |
| Imposed load. | 1.6 |
| Imposed load acting together with wind load. | 1.2 |
| Wind load. | 1.4 |
| Wind load acting together with imposed load. | 1.2 |
| Storage tanks, including contents. | 1.4 |
| Storage tanks, empty, when restraining sliding, overturning or uplift. | 1.0 |
| Earth and ground-water load, worst credible values, see §2.2.4. | 1.2 |
| Earth and ground-water load, nominal values, see §2.2.4. | 1.4 |
| Exceptional snow load (due to local drifting on roofs, see §4 in BS 6399–3:1998). | 1.05 |
| Forces due to temperature change. | 1.2 |

| | |
|---|---|
| Vertical crane loads. | 1.6 |
| Vertical crane loads acting together with horizontal crane loads. | 1.4* |
| Horizontal crane loads (surge, see §2.2.3, or crabbing, see §4.11.2). | 1.6 |
| Horizontal crane loads acting together with vertical crane loads. | 1.4 |
| Vertical crane loads acting together with imposed load. | 1.4* |
| Horizontal crane loads acting together with imposed load. | 1.2 |
| Imposed load acting together with vertical crane loads. | 1.4 |
| Imposed load acting together with horizontal crane loads. | 1.2 |
| Crane loads acting together with wind load. | 1.2* |
| Wind load acting together with crane loads. | 1.2 |

*Use $\gamma_f$ = 1.0 for vertical crane loads that counteract the effects of other loads.

The material factor $\gamma_m$ has been set as 1, so that the stress used for design, i.e. ($p_y$), is equal to the specified yield stress in the material standards giving the following design values:

BS 5950 Table 9. Design strengths, $p_y$, for steel to BS 4360

| Steel Grade* | Thickness, less than or equal to mm | Design strength $p_y$ N/mm$^2$ |
|---|---|---|
| S 275 | 16 | 275 |
| | 40 | 265 |
| | 63 | 255 |
| | 80 | 245 |
| | 100 | 235 |
| | 150 | 225 |
| S 355 | 16 | 355 |
| | 40 | 345 |
| | 63 | 335 |
| | 80 | 325 |
| | 100 | 315 |
| | 150 | 295 |

| Steel Grade* | Thickness, less than or equal to mm | Design strength $p_y$ N/mm² |
|---|---|---|
| S 460 | 16 | 460 |
| | 40 | 440 |
| | 63 | 430 |
| | 80 | 410 |
| | 100 | 400 |

* Continental steels are also regularly produced in grade S 235, but these are not common in the UK and Ireland. They are therefore not mentioned in BS 5950.

It is expected that such values of partial safety and stress factors will give structures the same level of safety as those already standing which have been designed to previous codes. The limit states approach gives a more consistent level of safety, so the extremes of overdesign and underdesign have been reduced.

## 3.3. Safe design

One might ask why there should be a gap between the loads applied to the structure and the factored loads used in the design. Surely the structure would be more economic if lower factors were used and the stresses were closer to the yield stress?

The chief reason for this margin is the desire of the designer to produce safe structures, and in order to do that he has to allow for certain contingencies. These include:

- Approximation and uncertainties in the method of analysis
- Accidental errors in design or stress calculation
- Imperfections of material and/or workmanship
- Accidental overloading during construction or otherwise
- Additional stresses due to changes of temperature or slight unequal subsidence of supports
- Corrosion

In the case of gross errors or imperfections, the normal factors of safety will not necessarily produce safe structures, so that it is incumbent on the designer and builder to ensure that all reasonable steps are undertaken to ensure that there are no major errors in design and construction. It is also important for the building owner to realise that he must not overload the structure by changing the use.

Let us consider the above in slightly greater detail.

*Approximations and uncertainties in the method of analysis*

A floor load, for example, may be assumed to be a constant number of kN on each square metre, even though, in practice, no floor is ever loaded uniformly.

Similarly, the pressure exerted on a building by wind may be assumed to be constant in time and distributed uniformly over its surface. However, gusting is a feature of wind effects and wind pressure varies from point to point of a building.

*Accidental errors in design or stress calculation*

Strictly speaking there should be no errors in the design, but it is accepted that in practice faults in design do occur. Simplifying approximations, for example, in stanchion design, can cause errors in calculation.

*Imperfections of material and/or workmanship*

Let us consider first imperfections of material. Despite the routine testing, occasionally some material with a yield stress lower than specified is used. If every time this occurred a failure of a structure resulted then the number of failures would certainly be far more than it is at present.

Also, the process of rolling leaves the sections produced with residual stresses, due on the one hand to this deformation and on the other hand to the unequal cooling of different portions of the sections. Without going into the matter in great detail, it can be said that the presence of these stresses may, under certain circumstances, weaken the members and it is as well to know of their existence. The code rules allow for the general case of these imperfections.

Let us now examine imperfections of workmanship. Bad fabrication would come under this heading. For example, if the ends of stanchions at a splice are not properly aligned and the ends of the two lengths are not in full contact with each other, excessive concentration of stress will be developed where contact is made.

Examples of bad workmanship also appear in welded work. Faults may arise in the execution of welds, which may be due to poor equipment, poor access for the welder, or inadequate care and skill by the welder himself.

Bad erection may also be included under this subdivision. For example, if bolts of an incorrect size are used the strength of the connection is not properly developed.

### Accidental overloading during construction or otherwise

Overloading should not occur but occasionally it does. It may happen that the floor of a building intended for a load of, say, 4 kN/m$^2$ is loaded up with a heap of bricks and sand to a height of one metre, so producing locally an actual loading greater than that for which the structure was designed.

Alternatively, a floor designed for a light load may have a heavy safe wheeled across it.

### Additional stresses due to changes of temperature or slight unequal subsidence of supports

An example of the first has already been mentioned, i.e. the unequal cooling of sections after rolling.

### Corrosion

Guidance is now available regarding the protection required to ensure adequate life between periods of maintenance for structural steel in various conditions. These should be followed to ensure that corrosion is not a critical limit state.

Experience, unfortunately, has shown that however much care is adopted, some of the defects referred to cannot be entirely avoided under practical conditions. The actual margin is a reasonable amount determined by practice, and this has been progressively reduced with increasing knowledge of structural theory and materials technology, and improved supervision.

# 4. Loads

## 4.1. General notes

Structures must safely carry all loads imposed on them and, therefore, knowledge of the expected maximum loads and load combinations is essential to the design process.

The determination of these loads is a complex problem because the nature of the loads varies with the design, the materials and the location of the structures. Also, loading conditions on the same structure may change from time to time, or may change rapidly with time.

Designers, therefore, must determine the rational combination of loads that will produce maximum stresses or deflections in various parts of the structure.

The most important loads carried by a building structure do not, normally, change rapidly with time; these are called static loads and form the basis for the structure's design.

To simplify the design of common structures, codes specify minimum design loads for the various types of use. The magnitude of these has been established mainly by many years of practice and experience, and to a lesser extent by research investigations and by statistical and probabilistic evaluations. From time to time, the design loads are modified as new knowledge is acquired and new conditions arise.

Although the load values given in codes are usually the acceptable minimum, they sometimes serve only as guides. In some cases even such load values may be insufficient; for example, the snow load or wind load on a novel, curved roof is highly variable. The wind pressure on tall structures cannot be described in general terms for it depends on a great number of factors. Aerospace installations are subjected to unique loadings that are not covered in any code and the effect of the wind load may have to be determined by means of tests on models, conducted in a wind tunnel.

It is essential that designers are aware of the relationship between actual loads and specified loads, since the responsibility for the adequacy of the design rests with them even if they have used the specified design loads of the appropriate code.

## 4.2. Dead load

The weight of the structure itself and the weight of all loads permanently on it constitute its dead load.

The dimensions of a structural element depend essentially on the loads acting upon it. The dead load, which is part of the applied load, depends on the dimensions of the element. Provisional dimensions are therefore taken in order to obtain a value for the dead load. Once the dimensions of a structure have been determined, its weight is evaluated by consulting tables of unit weights for the various structural materials. Some typical values for preliminary design are tabulated below.

| Material | Density $kg/m^3$ |
| --- | --- |
| Plain concrete | 2 300 |
| Reinforced concrete | 2 400 |
| Structural steel | 7 850 |
| Aluminium | 2 700 |
| Timber | 300 to 900 |
| Brickwork | 1 600 to 2 400 |
| Blockwork | Up to 1 600 |

To this dead load, designers add all the other loads, check the strength of the structure they have designed, and at the very end of their calculations see if their provisional dimensions were correct. With experience and practice, designers can almost invariably guess the weight of a member with sufficient accuracy that not more than one trial design usually needs to be made. But for other than routine cases, a re-evaluation of the dead load may be necessary, which may lead to a redesign of the structure.

For the purpose of structural analysis, loads are usually idealised as one of three kinds:

- Concentrated or point loads that are single forces acting over a relatively small area; for example, vehicle wheel loads, column loads or the force exerted by a beam connected to another beam at right angles.

- Line loads that act along a line; for example, loads exerted by a train or the weight of a partition resting on a floor slab.
- Distributed loads that act over a surface area. Most loads are distributed or treated as such; for example, wind pressure, soil pressure or the weight of floors and roofing materials.

The dead load is, in some cases, the most important load on a structure; for example in bridges and in roofs over wide areas, the dead load frequently dictates the choice of the materials.

In a few cases, the dead load is not only important but is useful and may contribute to the overall stability of a structure; for example, in gravity dams and Gothic buttresses.

Modern structural materials, such as high strength steel, prestressed concrete or aluminium, may reduce the importance of the dead load in relation to other loads, but the dead load is always present, is a permanent load, and should, therefore, be carefully estimated.

## 4.3. Live load

All loads other than dead load on a structure are called live load. They include all movable weights, such as occupants, machinery and vehicles. Materials in storage, removable partitions and furnishings must also be included. Allowance must also be made for the effects of loads such as rain, snow, ice, wind, water, fluids and soil.

Building codes always give rules for the dead and live load, and one code predominantly used in Britain and Ireland is BS 6399: Part 1 for imposed loads, Part 2 for wind loads and Part 3 for roof loads. BS CP3 Chapter V: Part 2 is still sometimes used for wind loading, although it is obsolescent.

### 4.3.1. Imposed load

BS 6399–1:1996 indicates floor loadings for various usages, gives an interpretation of the terminology for loading and covers in great detail most of the conditions likely to be met in design problems. Some of the imposed loads on floors are as follows:

| | |
|---|---|
| For dwellings | 1.5 kN/m$^2$ |
| For classrooms | 3.0 kN/m$^2$ |
| For bedrooms of hotels | 2.0 kN/m$^2$ |
| For offices (general use) | 2.5 kN/m$^2$ |
| For offices with filing | 5.0 kN/m$^2$ |
| For flat roofs (up to 10° pitch) | 0.75 kN/m$^2$ |
| For roofs where access is provided | 1.5 kN/m$^2$ |

In a multi-storey building, the probability of having the full imposed load on the entire floor on all storeys is unlikely and to take this fact into account, the code contains provisions for the reduction of imposed load.

Note the dead load should never be reduced, except in cases where it resists uplift or overturning, when BS 5950 specifically gives reduced safety factors.

### 4.3.2. Wind load

BS 6399: Part 2 deals with all the loads due to the effect of wind pressure or suction.

The effect of wind on structures depends principally on the kinetic energy possessed by the wind, by reason of the mass and velocity of the moving air, and on the building shape, exposure, orientation with respect to wind direction and degree of openness.

From the variables mentioned, it is evident that it is difficult to arrive at practical standards for wind design, because winds do not remain constant in terms of mass, velocity, direction or angle of incidence, even for a given geographic locality; also buildings vary widely in their shape, and in terms of the number, size and location of openings or potential openings. Furthermore, no two buildings share a common exterior physical environment, nor can it be assumed that a given environment will remain unchanged with the passage of time; for example, adjacent structures may increase or decrease in number or be altered or replaced by structures of different size and shape.

Nevertheless, a rational design procedure must be evolved, and codes prescribe safe, uniform pressures or suctions due to wind; these are revised from time to time in order to take into account the further knowledge accumulated in the field of aerodynamics.

CP3 Chapter V: Part 2 was under revision for a long time and BS 6399: Part 2 was published in 1997. Initially the two were to run in parallel for a two-year period. However, this was extended for a further two years as a result of pressure from the industry.

## 4.4. Dynamic loading

Loads that change magnitude rapidly or are applied suddenly are called dynamic loads. Their action must be clearly understood because, in certain circumstances, they can cause unusual effects.

The common experience of driving in a nail by giving it a hammer blow indicates that applying a load suddenly achieves results unobtainable by applying the same load slowly.

Also, if somebody wants to ring a heavy church bell he pulls its rope rhythmically; the bell starts to swing progressively until, eventually, it rings.

The force exerted by the hammer blow is called an *impact load*; the rhythmic pull of the rope is a *resonant load*.

Dynamic loads are exerted on structures in various ways. A sudden gust of wind is similar to a hammer blow. A company of soldiers marching in step exerts a resonant load on a bridge, when their step is in rhythm with the oscillations of the bridge. Some old, small bridges are known to have collapsed under such resonant loads.

However, only in a few instances it is necessary to allow for the dynamic effects of loads in architectural structures. Loads from earthquakes, moving or heavy vibrating machinery and wind loads on flexible structures are considered as dynamic loads. However, these occur under exceptional conditions in architectural structures and do not enter into the design of simple buildings in the UK and Ireland.

All dynamic phenomena are complex but designers must be aware of their action if they are to avoid failures. The most notable failure in recent times due to resonant dynamic phenomena was that of the first Tacoma Narrow Bridge (Washington) in 1940, where a wind of 68 km/h blowing continuously for 6 hours, set up oscillations which increased steadily in magnitude, twisting and bending the bridge until it collapsed. The amplitude of some of these oscillations was up to 3 m in depth.

## 4.5. Loading induced by temperature shrinkage, settlement and improper fit

Finally, mention must be made of the forces that may be created in structures when provision is not made for relative movements between various points in the structure. Such relative movements may be developed as a result of temperature changes, shrinkage, or settlement of some of the supports. These loads should be considered, because surprisingly large forces may result in structural components where unrestrained expansion or contraction cannot occur.

A simple example will suffice to indicate the nature and importance of this type of loading. A steel bridge, spanning 30 m, was built in winter where, say, the temperature was just above freezing point. On a hot August day, the temperature can reach 30 °C (86 °F). The increase in length of the bridge, which may be calculated, is only about 30 mm, which is very small in comparison to the 30 m span of the bridge. But if this expansion cannot take place, a horizontal compressive force is developed, unless expansion joints are provided. This force is so large that it would cause a compressive stress equal to about half the yield strength of the steel.

In the design of large structures, it is customary to design expansion joints to allow the structure to 'breathe' under temperature variation or shrinkage without straining and cracking.

Stresses may also result from improper fit, i.e. when a member of improper size is forced into place during construction.

## 4.6. Summary

To summarise this important step in the design process, i.e. the determination of loads, designers should follow the recommended code loads for routine cases. However, for unusual or special structures, the load analysis may require extensive study.

In every case the designers must ascertain the expected loads, their relative importance and the associated structural performance, because they alone are responsible for their designs including the loads that they have chosen to use.

# 5.  Plastic analysis and design

## 5.1. Introduction

Of the many functional requirements that an engineering structure has to satisfy, two of the most important ones are strength and stiffness. The strength requirement is that the structure shall be strong enough to resist the external loading and its own weight without collapsing. The stiffness requirement is that the structure shall be stiff enough in order not to deflect excessively under the total loading.

In structural design to *simple theory* there is little interaction between the elements of the structure. In the design of continuous structures this is not so, the stiffness and position of each member having a profound effect on the behaviour of the structure as a whole. In plastic design the ductility of the steel is also considered during the design process to determine the ultimate capacity of the structures.

Tests on actual buildings during the mid 1930s, such as those carried out by the Steel Structures Research Committee, made it clear that a steel frame behaves differently from the assumptions made in the simple design of the day. In some cases the real factor of safety of structural elements was shown to be very different from that which had been assumed. The adoption of revised design rules and a limit state approach has done much in BS 5950 to remedy this situation.

After 1936, when the the Committee's report was published, work started on the development of what was to become our present day *plastic theory*, which was first allowed in BS 449:1948. Until the publication of BS 5950 in 1985 the method was allowed with a 'suitable factor of safety' but with no real practical design help. BS 5950 now gives positive guidance to the design engineer on how to carry out the design of continuous struc-tures, including plastic design.

Simple plastic theory is concerned with the ultimate strength of struc-tures; thus, if a steel-framed structure is analysed by this method, the values of the loads which will cause it to collapse will be determined. When plastic theory is used in design the required reserve of strength against collapse is obtained by designing the structure to fail under factored loads, which are obtained using Table 2 of BS 5950. Therefore, in plastic design (also called collapse, ultimate-load or load factor design) the factored loads must be less than the collapse load of the structure.

Plastic theory makes the design process more rational, since the level of safety is related to the collapse load on the structure and not to the apparent failure at one point. It will be found that the plastic collapse load on the structure is independent of the sinking of the supports or the flexibility of the connections. But it must be pointed out that the structure may be subjected to P∆ effects, which occur when the frame is free to sway side-ways under vertical as well as horizontal loads. BS 5950 gives rules to ensure that such modes of failure do not happen; except for portal frames, these rules are not considered to be within the scope of the present book.

In some cases plastic methods may be found to be easier to apply than elastic methods. The frame and its components must be checked rigorously for overall and local stability because of the high strains that have to be considered.

## 5.2. Basis of plastic theory

If a short length of Universal Beam is subjected to a gradually increasing bending moment and the values of curvature, defined as the reciprocal of the radius of curvature, are measured then a curve will be obtained, as shown in Fig. 5.1(a). The portion CD, a slight rising curve, is due to strain hardening.

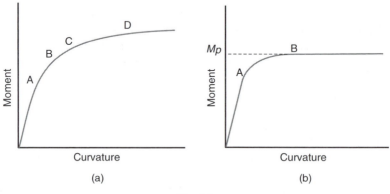

*Fig. 5.1.*

For the purposes of simple plastic theory it is conservatively assumed that a maximum moment, $M_p$, is reached at which curvature can increase indefinitely (see Fig. 5.1(b)). The maximum moment, $M_p$, is known as the full plastic moment and the portion of the member at which that occurs is known as a plastic hinge, and can sustain large local increases of curvature.

Axial loads and shear forces, unless large in relation to the section being used, have only a small effect on the bending strength of the section.

The fundamental concept of the plastic method is that sufficient plastic hinges are imagined to occur at critical sections to develop a collapse mechanism. The justification of this concept is to be found in the results of many tests on beams and framed structures.

## 5.3. Brief historical review

The first published papers on the subject were those of Gabor Kazinczy, published in Hungary in 1914. Kazinczy carried out some tests on fixed-ended beams and came to the conclusion that failure took place only when yielding had occurred at three cross-sections, at which a hinging action could be said to take place. He may, therefore, be considered as the originator of the plastic methods, because of the fundamentally important concept of the plastic hinge.

After Kazinczy, several German and Dutch engineers dealt with plastic methods applied to beams, continuous beams and simple frames. The best known of the Dutch engineers was NC Kist, but the most famous engineer was the German, Maier-Leibnitz, who showed that the ultimate capacity of continuous beams was not affected by settlement of supports. In 1936, he also collected the results of all the principal tests carried out to that point and published them in his famous paper to the Berlin International Congress of Engineers.

During the same year (1936), the Steel Structures Research Committee in England put forward the so-called 'semi-rigid' method of designing structures, but this was fairly complex and never really found favour with the steel industry. In any case, the economy resulting from this method was very small.

Thus far, the analytical developments were directed towards refining the theory based on the concept of the plastic hinge.

In 1938 JF Baker (the late Lord Baker of Windrush) of Cambridge was the first to realise that simple plastic theory might be used for the design of complex frames. A team of British engineers under him, including Professor Horne and Professor Heyman, subsequently evolved the method in which the collapse loads are considered as the design criteria.

In the USA, Van den Broek wrote the first published paper on plastic theory in 1939.

These, and other subsequent contributions, placed the plastic methods on a firm footing and the mathematical theory has now been developed to cover a wide range of structures.

## 5.4. Conditions and methods of plastic analysis

### 5.4.1. Basic methods of analysis

In the elastic analysis of a hyperstatic structure under static loading, three conditions must be considered:

- Continuity. The deflected shape is assumed to be a continuous curve and thus *continuity equations* may be formulated with due regard to boundary conditions.
- Equilibrium. The summation of the forces and moments acting on any free body must be equal to zero.
- Limiting moment. The moment at first yield is the limiting moment, i.e. nowhere must the moments be greater than the yield moment.

In the plastic analysis the three conditions that must be satisfied are:

- The mechanism condition. The ultimate load is reached when a mechanism is formed.
- The equilibrium condition. Equilibrium of moments and forces must apply.
- The plastic moment conditions. The moments in the structure must nowhere be greater than the plastic moment of the section. $M \leq M_P$

There are two basic methods of plastic analysis. One method assumes a mechanism and uses the virtual work equations to determine the collapse load.

This is known as the *mechanism* or *kinematic* method.

The other method uses a moment diagram which has all the moments less than or equal to the plastic moment and where equilibrium is satisfied.

This is known as the *statical* or *equilibrium method*.

Two theorems are available which provide bounds for both methods. These are known as the upper and lower bound theorems.

The *upper bound theorem* states that a load computed on the basis of an assumed mechanism will always be greater, or at best equal to, the correct collapse load.

The *lower bound theorem* states that a load computed on the basis of an assumed equilibrium moment diagram, in which moments are nowhere greater than the plastic moment, is less, or at best equal to, the correct collapse load.

The mechanism method uses the upper bound theorem, while the equilibrium method uses the lower bound theorem.

Note: The upper and lower bound theorems can be combined to produce a new theorem, sometimes known as the uniqueness theorem. It simply states that the load which satisfies both theorems at the same time is the correct collapse load.

### 5.4.2. Formation of plastic hinges

In order to make the understanding and calculation simpler, it may be assumed that the members are rigid between supports and hinge positions. This assumption is approximately correct because of the relatively low deformations which occur in the elastic range. By applying the theorem of virtual work, the energy dissipated in the members represented by the rotation ($\theta$) times the plastic moment capacity of the section ($M_p$) must be balanced by the energy applied by the force, i.e. load times distance. This is demonstrated in Fig. 5.3.

Consideration of the behaviour of a beam will show that under load the straining will take place at the centre of the span where the hinge is formed. The remainder of the section will remain sensibly straight, thus the energy in the structure will be absorbed in the hinge (see Fig. 5.2).

The moment diagram is compared to the moment/rotation curve for the section. The part where there is plasticity, shown by the non-linear behaviour of this curve, may be projected onto the moment diagram, assuming that the full plastic moment has been attained. This may then be projected onto the section and the area of plasticity determined. At the centre of the area there will be full plasticity over the full depth of the section, resulting in a plastic hinge.

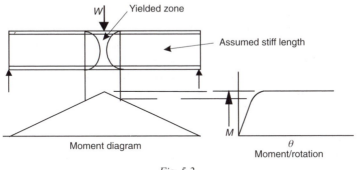

*Fig. 5.2.*

It is shown in Fig. 5.3 that it is possible to use this method to derive a well-known value for the maximum span moment in a simple case. It is this result which gives the maximum moment capacity of a simply supported beam with a central point load.

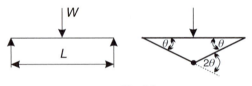

*Fig. 5.3.*

Work in hinge $= 2M_p\theta$

Work by load $= \dfrac{WL}{2}\theta$

At collapse, work in hinge = work by load

$$\therefore 2M_p\,\theta = \frac{WL}{2}\,\theta$$

$$\therefore W = \frac{4M_p}{L}\ \text{or}\ M_p = \frac{WL}{4}$$

*Example 5.4.1. The propped cantilever shown in Fig. 5.4(a) is made of a section with a plastic moment, $M_p$. Determine the collapse load, W.*

### Using the mechanism method

The possible mechanisms that need investigation are shown in Fig. 5.4(b), (c) and (d). The plastic hinges are located at points of maximum moments. Consider the mechanism shown in (b). Suppose at collapse load it is allowed to move through a small vertical displacement. If the rotation at D is called $\theta$, then the resultant geometry can be defined in terms of $\theta$. Since the beam is in equilibrium the virtual displacement method can be applied.

The external work is that done by the loads at B and C travelling through $\delta_B$ and $\delta_C$ respectively.

$\delta_B = 3 \times 2\theta$ and $\delta_C = 3 \times \theta$

The total external work ($W_e$) becomes:

$$W_e = \underset{\uparrow}{W \times 3 \times 2\theta} + \underset{\uparrow}{W \times 3\theta} = \underset{\uparrow}{W \times 9\theta}$$

$\qquad\qquad$ At section B $\qquad$ At section C $\qquad$ Total

The internal work is that done by the plastic moments rotating through their respective angles. The total internal work becomes:

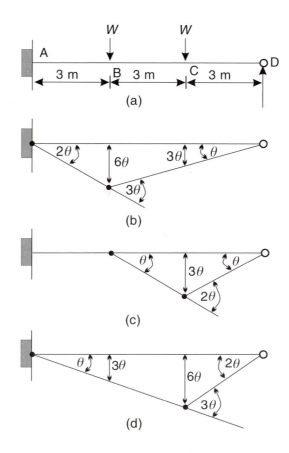

*Fig. 5.4.*

$$W_i \quad = \quad M_p \times 2\theta \quad + \quad M_p \times 3\theta \quad = \quad M_p \times 5\theta$$

| | At section A | At section B | Total |

Equating the expressions for work:

$$W \times 9\theta = M_p \times 5\theta$$

$$W = \frac{5}{9} M_p$$

$$= 0.55 M_p$$

The same technique applied to the mechanism shown in Fig. 5.4(c) gives:

$$W_e = W \times 3\theta \text{ at section C}$$

$$W_i = \underset{\underset{\text{At section B}}{\uparrow}}{M_p \times \theta} + \underset{\underset{\text{At section C}}{\uparrow}}{M_p \times 2\theta} = \underset{\underset{\text{Total}}{\uparrow}}{M_p \times 3\theta}$$

Equating the expressions for work:

$$W \times 3\theta = M_p \times 3\theta$$

$$W = M_p$$

Similarly for the mechanism shown in Fig. 5.4(d):

$$W_e = \underset{\underset{\text{At section B}}{\uparrow}}{W \times 3\theta} + \underset{\underset{\text{At section C}}{\uparrow}}{W \times 3 \times 2\theta} = \underset{\underset{\text{Total}}{\uparrow}}{W \times 9\theta}$$

$$W_i = \underset{\underset{\text{At section A}}{\uparrow}}{M_p \theta} + \underset{\underset{\text{At section B}}{\uparrow}}{M_p \times 3\theta} = \underset{\underset{\text{Total}}{\uparrow}}{M_p \times 4\theta}$$

Equating the expressions for work:

$$9W\theta = 4M_p\theta$$

$$W = \frac{4}{9} M_p$$

$$= 0.44M_p$$

Comparing the three results shows that the mechanism in Fig. 5.4(d) produced the lowest collapse load. Since all possible mechanisms have been examined the collapse load for the beam is $W = \frac{4}{9} M_p$ or $0.44M_p$.

The correct location of the plastic hinges is a prior requirement of the mechanism method. Incorrect locations predict loads greater than the correct collapse load. Hinges will form at points of maximum moment, which occur at the supports, under concentrated loads, and at the position of zero shear force within a span.

### Using the structural equilibrium method

The lower bound theorem is used in the construction of an equilibrium moment diagram in which the moments nowhere exceed the plastic moment of resistance of the section, but which have sufficient plastic hinges to produce a mechanism. Fig. 5.5(b) shows an equilibrium diagram. The beam requires two further hinges to form a mechanism.

Examining the moment diagram for the two points where hinges are most likely to occur leads to A and C as the moment diagram peaks at these locations. Fig. 5.5(c) is the same moment diagram redrawn so that the moments at A and C are equal. The free moment (simply supported beam moment) at C is $3W$. The same height can be represented by $M_p + \frac{1}{3}M_p$, i.e. $\frac{4}{3}M_p$.

$$3W = \frac{4}{3}M_p$$

$$\therefore W = \frac{4}{9}M_p$$

$$= 0.44M_p$$

The corresponding mechanism is shown in Fig. 5.5(d).

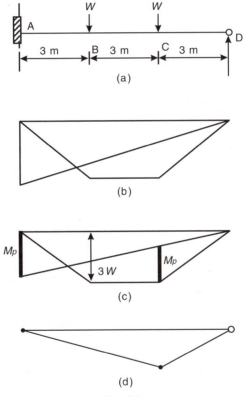

(a)

(b)

(c)

(d)

*Fig. 5.5.*

## 5.5. Examination of a beam under bending

When a beam is subjected to bending, the strain distribution at any particular cross-section is linear, i.e. the strain is proportional to the distance of the fibres from the neutral axis.

Depending upon the stress level, the bending may be (i) fully elastic, (ii) elastoplastic, or (iii) fully plastic.

### Fully elastic bending

If all sections of a beam remain in the elastic range, the stress in any fibre is proportional to the strain in it and hence to its distance from the neutral axis. The stress distribution across the section of maximum bending moment for a rectangular beam in the elastic range is shown in Fig. 5.6(a).

In elastic design methods, the permissible extreme stress is restricted to a proportion of the yield stress, $f_y$, which for S 275 steel is 165 N/mm$^2$.

The basic formula used for elastic bending is:

$$\frac{f}{y} = \frac{M}{I} \text{ or } M = fZ$$

where:

$Z$ is the elastic modulus of the section
$y$ is the half depth of a symmetrical section

For the rectangular beam shown,

$$M = f \times \frac{b \times d^2}{6} \tag{5.I}$$

where $f$ is less than $f_y$.

### Elastoplastic or partially plastic bending

When the beam is subjected to a moment slightly greater than that which first produces yield in the extreme fibres the outer fibres yield at constant stress, $f_y$, while the fibres nearer to the neutral axis (NA) sustain increased elastic stress. Fig. 5.6(b) shows the appropriate stress distribution. The portions of the beam which have reached the yield stress are described as *plastic zones*.

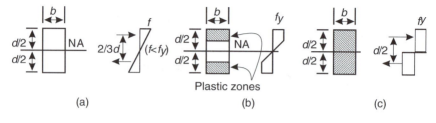

*Fig. 5.6.*

### Fully plastic bending

As the moment is further increased, the plastic zones increase in depth until eventually they may be considered to meet the NA, one zone yielding in compression and the other in tension. The beam is now fully plastic at the section considered and the stress distribution is shown in Fig. 5.6(c).

The greatest moment of resistance that a beam can exert at full plasticity is called the *Plastic Moment of Resistance* (PMR) and depends on the dimensions of the section and the magnitude of the yield stress.

PMR is equated to $M_p$ and for a rectangular section, such as the one used here,

$$\text{PMR} = C \times a = T \times a \qquad (5.\text{II})$$

where:

$C$ is compression
$T$ is tension
$a$ is the lever arm

Substituting the appropriate values:

$$
\begin{aligned}
PMR &= f_y \times b \times \frac{d}{2} \times \frac{d}{2} \\
&= f_y \times b \times \frac{d^2}{4}
\end{aligned}
\qquad (5.\text{III})
$$

Notice the lever arm of the couple changes from $\frac{2}{3} d$ in the elastic stress condition to $\frac{1}{2} d$ in the plastic condition.

The first moment of area $S$ of the section about its axis of symmetry is as follows:

$$S = 2 \times b \times \frac{d}{2} \times \frac{d}{4} = b \times \frac{d^2}{4}$$

Therefore

$$\text{PMR} = f_y \times S \qquad (5.\text{IV})$$

It can be stated as a general rule that the above equation will apply for any symmetrical section. Since $MR = f_y \times Z$ in elastic design, by analogy the quantity $S$ is called the *plastic modulus* of the section.

The ratio $S/Z$ is known as the shape factor of the section and is usually identified by $v$.

For a rectangular beam $v = \dfrac{S}{Z} = \dfrac{\dfrac{bd^2}{4}}{\dfrac{bd^2}{6}} = 1.5$

For I-sections, $v$ is approximately 1.15.

The form of the moment/curvature relationship is shown in Fig. 5.7.

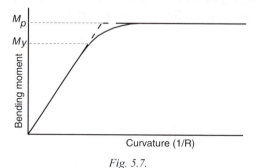

Fig. 5.7.

In most calculations, the moment/curvature relationship is approximated by two straight lines, as shown by broken lines. This is termed the *ideal plastic relation*. The same approach may be applied to the calculation of the fully plastic moment of resistance of a symmetrical I-section.

The shape factor, $v = \dfrac{S}{Z}$ can also be expressed by the ratio $\dfrac{M_p}{M_y}$,

i.e. multiplying by $f_y$ top and bottom, $M_y = \dfrac{1}{v} M_p$.

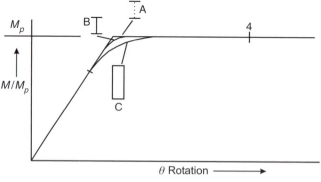

Fig. 5.8.

An idealised section which provides a useful mathematical model for elastoplastic behaviour is a twin-plate section ( $\overline{\underline{\cdot}}$ ) consisting of two plates, each of area $A/2$, distance apart $d$, with a web of zero area.

For such a theoretical section, $Z = S = \frac{1}{2}Ad$; i.e. the shape factor is unity.

Fig. 5.8 shows a plot of the moment/curvature relationships for three sections.

BS 5950 makes allowance for the high level of strains involved in plastic analysis by imposing the following criteria on the steel:

- The ultimate tensile strain is at least 20 times the strain at first yield.
- The ultimate tensile strength is at least 1.2 times the yield strength.
- The elongation on a gauge length of $5.65\sqrt{A_o}$ is at least fifteen per cent, where $A_o$ is the area of the unstrained test specimen

In the following examples reference is made to reactant diagrams; these are the moment diagrams derived from moments at the supports resulting from the continuity of the members.

*Example 5.5.1. Design a propped cantilever, 6 m span, carrying an unfactored concentrated load of 150 kN, 2 m from the fixed end. Self-weight may be neglected. The load is assumed to be 50% dead and 50% imposed load. The steel is to be grade S 275.*

SOLUTION

| Imposed load | $= 50\%$ of 150 kN $= 75$ kN | $= 120$ kN factored ($\gamma_f = 1.6$) |
|---|---|---|
| Dead load | $= 50\%$ of 150 kN $= 75$ kN | $= 105$ kN factored ($\gamma_f = 1.4$) |
| Total factored load | | $= 225$ kN |

Using the mechanism method

Possible mechanism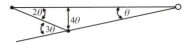

Work dissipated at a plastic hinge is equal to the product of the full plastic moment and the hinge rotation.

$$\text{Total work dissipated, } W_i = M_p \times 2\theta + M_p \times 3\theta = M_p \times 5\theta$$

$$\text{Work done by load external work, } W_e = 225 \times 4\theta = 900\theta$$

$$\text{Equating the work, } M_p \times 5 = 900$$

Bending moment diagram

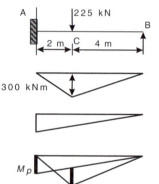

$M_p$

∴ $M_p = 180$ kNm

$$S_{x\,(required)} = 180 \times \frac{10^3}{275} = 655 \text{ cm}^3$$

A suitable section is a $406 \times 140 \times 39$ UB, $S_x = 724$ cm$^3$.

*Statical method*

Free bending moment $= 225 \times 2 \times \dfrac{4}{6}$

$= 300$ kNm

300 kNm

Reactant or fixing bending moment

Superimposing the two diagrams, $M_p$ at A is equal to $M_p$ at C.

$M_p$

$M_p$

$$M_p \text{ at C} = 300 - \frac{4}{6}M_p$$

$$= 300 - \frac{2}{3}M_p$$

$$\frac{5}{3}M_p = 300$$

$$\therefore M_p = 180 \text{ kNm}$$

$$S_{x\,(required)} = 180 \times \frac{10^3}{275} = 655 \text{ cm}^3$$

Use $406 \times 140 \times 39$ UB, $S_x = 724$ cm$^3$.

This section is the same as that derived from the mechanism method, illustrating the compatibility of the two methods, if used correctly.

*Example 5.5.2. Find a suitable section for a propped cantilever, 6 m span, carrying a factored load of 360 kN in grade S 275 steel.*

### SOLUTION

The bending moment diagram is once again made up from two components, a free moment and a reactant moment.

Note: The reactant diagram, or fixing bending moment diagram, is the same as before; it is purely a function of the structure not the loading.

It may be demonstrated that the maximum moment in plastic analysis for a beam fixed at one end and free at the other is $WL/11.66$ or $0.686\,WL/8$. Where $W$ is the total factored load.

The distance from the fixed end to the point of maximum moment is $0.586L$.

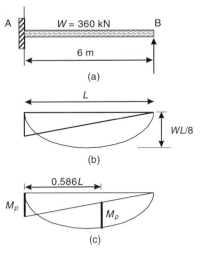

$$M_p = \frac{WL}{11.66} = \frac{360 \times 6}{11.66} = 185.25 \text{ kNm}$$

$$S_{x\,(required)} = 185.25 \times \frac{10^3}{275} = 674 \text{ cm}^3$$

A $406 \times 140 \times 39$ UB has a value of $S_x = 724$ cm³. This will be adequate.

## 5.6. The effect of axial load on moment capacity

*Effect of axial load*

Denoting axial load by $F$, acting at the centreline of the cross-section, the theory for a simple rectangular section is as follows:

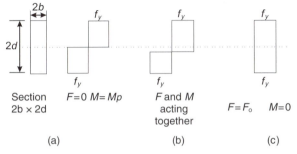

*Fig. 5.9.*

The three diagrams in Fig. 5.9 indicate different combinations of axial load and bending moment consistent with full section plasticity.
With $F = 0$:

$$M_p = 2b \times d \times d \times f_y = 2bd^2 f_y$$

With $M = 0$:

$$F = F_0 = (2b \times 2d) \times f_y = 4bd f_y$$

where:

$F_0 = $ *squash load* or load at yield

The values of $M$ and $F$ necessary to cause full plasticity, if they are acting simultaneously, can be obtained from a consideration of the stress distribution, see Fig. 5.9(b). (Note that all moments are taken about the original equal area axis (chain dotted line) for consistency.)

Fig. 5.9(b) is equivalent to Fig. 5.10(a) and (b), the reduced bending moment and the axial load.

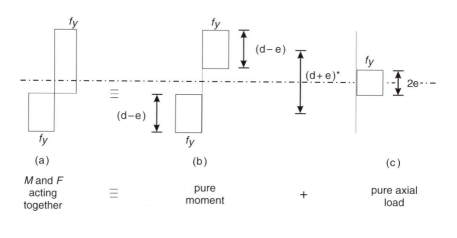

$$*\left[ \frac{(d-e)}{2} + 2e + \frac{(d-e)}{2} = (d-e) + 2e = d+e \right]$$

*Fig. 5.10.*

The reduced bending moment:

$$M = 2b(d - e)(d + e) \times f_y$$

$$M = 2bf_y(d^2 - e^2) = 2bd^2 f_y\left(1 - \frac{e^2}{d^2}\right) \qquad (5.V)$$

$$M = M_p\left(1 - \frac{e^2}{d^2}\right)$$

The axial load:

$$F = 2b \times 2e \times f_y = 4bef_y = 4bef_y\frac{d}{d}$$

$$F = 4bdf_y\frac{e}{d} = F_0\frac{e}{d} \qquad (5.VI)$$

$$\text{or } \frac{e}{d} = \frac{F}{F_0}$$

Equation (5.V) may be rewritten:

$$\frac{M}{M_p} = 1 - \frac{e^2}{d^2} = 1 - \left(\frac{e}{d}\right)^2$$

Substituting (5.VI) into the above expression:

$$\frac{M}{M_p} = 1 - \left(\frac{F}{F_0}\right)^2$$

$$\text{or } \frac{M}{M_p} + \left(\frac{F}{F_0}\right)^2 = 1$$

This is the formula for the effect of axial load on the plastic moment.

This formula can be plotted to give an interaction diagram, shown in Fig. 5.11.

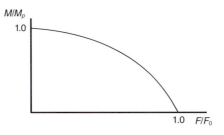

*Fig. 5.11.*

Note that the slope of this parabolic interaction diagram is zero at $M/M_p = 1.0$. In other words, the effect of axial load on the plastic moment is fairly small until substantial values of axial load are involved.

Note also that the slope at $F/F_0$ is not zero, but is, in fact, the angle of 63.5°.

$$\left[ \text{At } \frac{F}{F_0} = 1, \quad \frac{d\left(\frac{M}{M_P}\right)}{d\left(\frac{F}{F_0}\right)} = -2 \right]$$

[∴ angle with tan = −2 is 63.5°]

In other words, small values of moment will have noticeable effects on the 'squash load' of short columns.

Turning to the practical case of I-sections, the type of behaviour discussed above is again evident, with the additional complication that the zero stress axis of the distribution shown in Fig. 5.10(b) moves out of the web and into the flange for values of $F/F_0$ larger than a limiting value. This turns the interaction diagram of Fig. 5.11 into two curves rather than one, but the overall behaviour is very much the same. The resulting expressions are normally derived in terms of a parameter, $n$, which is the ratio of the axial load in the member to its squash load ($F/F_0$). Such expressions are given in section tables together with the value of $n$ at which the NA moves outside the web.

Note: In volume 1 of the guide to BS 5950, $n$ is given as

$$n = \frac{F}{A_g p_y}$$

so,

$$n = \frac{F}{A_g p_y} = \frac{F}{A_g \frac{F_0}{A_g}} = \frac{F}{F_0}$$

Selecting an example from these tables at random, say the 305 165 54 UB carrying an axial force $F$ of 603.8 kN.

$$F_0 = 1\,881 \text{ kN}$$

From this,

$$n = \frac{603.8}{1\,881} = 0.321$$

$$S_x = 845 \text{ cm}^3$$

For lower values of $n$, the reduced plastic modulus is

$$K1 - K2\, n^2 = 845 - 1\,510 \quad 0.321^2 = 845 - 156 = 689 \text{ cm}^3$$

If $n$ is 0.1, $S_r$ is only reduced by 15.1 cm$^3$

In single storey portal frames, it is found that the value of $n$ is usually less than 0.1, so that the effect of axial load will be small, unless the frame has some special features, such as crane bearing stanchions. However, in multi-storey frames, an allowance for the effect of axial load will often have to be made for stanchions in the lower storeys.

### Derivation of values of reduced plastic moduli

If the section tables are not available with the values of the constants required to determine the reduced plastic moduli then, for a section made up from rectangular plates, $M_{red}$ may be derived from the following equations:

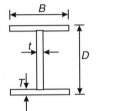

Low value of $n$ change point

$$M_{red} = K1 - K2\, n^2$$

High value of $n$ change point

$$M_{red} = K3\,(1 - n)\, K4(1 + n)$$

Where $n = \dfrac{F}{A_g p_y}$

*For major axis bending*
$K1 = S_x$
$K2 = A_g^2/4t$
$K3 = A_g^2/4B$
$K4 = 2BD/A_g - 1$

*For minor axis bending*
$K1 = S_y$
$K2 = A_g^2/4D$
$K3 = A_g^2/8T$
$K4 = 4TB/A_g - 1$

*Change point for the value of n*

$$n = \frac{(D - 2T)t}{A_g} \qquad n = \frac{Dt}{A_g}$$

In the above formulae, the dimensions of the section are as in the figure, with the following additions:

$S_x$ Plastic modulus about the major axis
$S_y$ Plastic modulus about the minor axis
$A_g$ Gross area of the section
$F$ Applied axial force
$p_y$ Design strength of the material

The above formulae are correct for sections made up from three plates and are sufficiently accurate for rolled universal beams and columns, with parallel flanges.

## 5.7. The effect of shear force on moment capacity

The effect of shear force on a beam of general cross-section is more complex than that of axial load. With axial load, the resulting stresses can be superimposed directly on the bending stresses, since they are all longitudinal.

Shear combined with bending gives rise to a two-dimensional stress system. (A general discussion of plastic behaviour under these conditions is outside the scope of this book.)

However, the special case of the I-section may be dealt with by an approximate method. If it is assumed that the shear stress is uniformly distributed over the web of an I-section, and that the flanges are not contributing at all to the carrying of the shear force, then an empirical solution in the plastic analysis of a problem may be obtained which gives good agreement with experimental results.

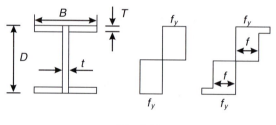

*Fig. 5.12.*

The full plastic moment $M_p$ of an I-rolled section, shown in Fig. 5.12, is given by:

$$M_p = (B - t)\,T\,(D - T)f_y + \frac{1}{4}D^2 tf_y$$

$$M_p = \underset{\text{flange}}{M_f} + \underset{\text{gross web}}{M_w}$$

Suppose now that a shear force, $F_v$, acts on the web causing a uniform shear stress, $\tau$, then:

$$\tau = \frac{F_v}{Dt}$$

If the web remains fully plastic, then the longitudinal stress, $f$, in the web available for resisting the bending moment will be reduced below the value $f_y$ (the yield stress).

There are several criteria for yield under combined stress systems; the criterion which fits best the experimental results for this problem is due to Mises, and in this simple case gives

$$f^2 + 3\tau^2 = f_y^2$$

$$\text{or} \quad \left(\frac{f}{f_y}\right)^2 + 3\left(\frac{\tau}{f_y}\right)^2 = 1$$

$$\text{or} \quad \frac{f}{f_y} = \sqrt{1 - 3\left(\frac{\tau}{f_y}\right)^2}$$

where:

$f$ is the stress available to resist the bending moment carried by the web
$\tau$ is the stress due to the shear force
$f_y$ is the design strength

The stress distribution over the cross-section under combined shear and bending sufficient to cause full plasticity will be as shown in Fig. 5.13.

$M_p$ then becomes:

$$M_p = M_f + M_w \frac{f}{f_y}$$

$$= M_f + M_w \sqrt{1 - 3\left(\frac{\tau}{f_y}\right)^2}$$

Note: This analysis may be applied to a built-up plate girder, using the net depth of the web in place of the total depth, or to a standard rolled section, the latter being approximated to three rectangles.

*Example 5.7.1. Suppose a 305 × 127 × 48 UB is subjected to a shear force of 200 kN and has a yield stress $f_y$ of, say, 250 N/mm², then,*

$$\tau = \frac{200 \times 10^3}{311 \times 9.0} = 71.5 \text{ N/mm}^2$$

$$\frac{f}{f_y} = \sqrt{1 - 3\left(\frac{71.5}{250}\right)^2} = 0.869$$

$$M_p = M_f + 0.869 M_w$$

This can be rewritten:

$$S_x = S_f + S_w$$

$$S_w = \frac{(310.4)^2 \times 8.9}{4 \times 10^3} = 214.4 \text{ cm}^3$$

$$S_x = S_f + 214.4$$

$$\text{or } S_f = S_x - 214.4$$

Under the action of the shear force:

$$S_{x \text{ (reduced)}} = S_f + 214\frac{f}{f_y}$$

$$= \left(S_x - 214\right) + 214\frac{f}{f_y}$$

$$= S_{x \text{ (original)}} - 214\left(1 - \frac{f}{f_y}\right)$$

$$S_{x \text{ (reduced)}} = S - 214 \times \left(1 - 0.869\right)$$

$$= 706 - 28.03$$

$$= 678 \text{ cm}^3$$

Note: Both axial load and shear force tend to lead to instability of the flanges and webs of I-sections, if the depth to thickness ratios of these are too large. Certain limits must therefore be imposed if full plasticity is to develop without the danger of local buckling. For limits, consult Table 11 of BS 5950.

Note: The shear area, $A_v$, for a rolled section is $tD$. For a welded I-section, however, $A_v$ is $td$ (see §4.2.3 and Figs. 4 and 5 of BS 5950).

BS 5950 has simplified the process described above by assuming that the moment capacity is not reduced if the shear force on the section is less than 0.6 of the maximum shear capacity of the section. If the shear force is

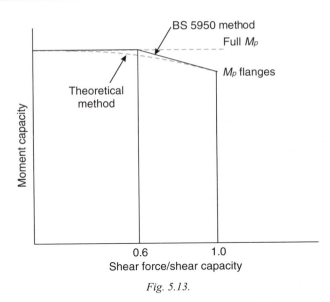

*Fig. 5.13.*

greater than this value then a linear reduction is made in moment capacity until full shear is reached. The effect of this procedure is shown in Fig. 5.13.

### Member stability

In addition to the requirement for simple members when using plastic design methods, it is expected that the points in the frame taken as plastic hinges will require additional restraint. This is because of the very high strains that occur when rotation is taking place as the frame approaches its ultimate load. The code, therefore, requires that both flanges are restrained at these points and that a limit is placed on the maximum distance to the next restraint on the member.

Restraints are dealt with in §5.3.3 and part of that clause is reproduced here.

Within a member containing a plastic hinge the maximum distance, $L_u$, from the hinge restraint to an adjacent restraint should be calculated by the following method.

Conservatively, $L_u$ (in mm) may be taken as:

$$L_u \leq \frac{38 r_y}{\left[ \dfrac{f_c}{130} + \left( \dfrac{p_y}{275} \right)^2 \left( \dfrac{x}{36} \right)^2 \right]^{0.5}}$$

where:

$f_c$  is the average compressive stress due to axial load (in N/mm$^2$)
$p_y$  is the design strength (in N/mm$^2$)
$r_y$  is the radius of gyration about the minor axis (in the same units as $L_u$)
$x$  is the torsional index (see Section 6.8 of this book)

Where the member has unequal flanges, $r_y$ should be taken as the lesser of the values for the compression flange only or the whole section.

Where the cross-section of the member varies within the length $L_u$, the minimum value of $r_y$ and the maximum value of $x$ should be used.

The spacing of restraints to member lengths not containing a plastic hinge should be such as to satisfy the recommendations of §4.3. Where the restraints are placed at the limiting distance $L_u$, no further checks are required for lateral torsional buckling.

## 5.8. Failure of a fixed ended beam under uniformly distributed load

Fig. 5.14(a) shows a fixed ended or built-in beam of span $L$ carrying a total UDL of $W$.

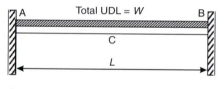

*Fig. 5.14(a)*

The fixed end moments are $WL/12$ at A and B and the mid-span moment at C is $WL/24$ (Fig. 5.14(b)).

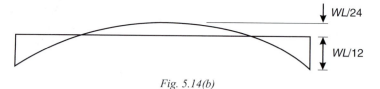

*Fig. 5.14(b)*

As the load is increased the extreme fibres yield at the ends of the beam, where the moment is greatest, and elastoplastic bending commences. Further increases of load cause plastic hinges at the ends (Fig. 5.14(c)). The formation of these hinges does not cause collapse because the beam is able to carry further load as a simply-supported beam; failure will occur when an increase in the load causes a third plastic hinge to form at mid-span, as shown in Fig. 5.14(d).

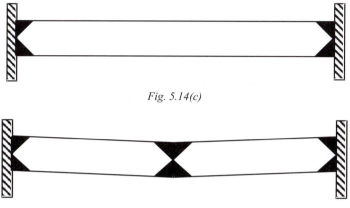

*Fig. 5.14(c)*

*Fig. 5.14(d)*

This beam may be analysed as follows: Let plastic moment of resistance of the beam be equal to $M_p p_y$ and $W_{col}$ equal to $\gamma_f W$ (where $W_{col}$ is the collapse load and $W$ is the working load).

If $W_1$ is that proportion of the load that causes plastic hinges to form at the ends of the beam, then the moment at the ends due to this load is $W_1 L/12$ and since a plastic hinge forms at the end,

$$M_p = \frac{W_1 L}{12} \tag{5.VII}$$

The mid-span moment is now $W_1 L/24$.

Let the additional load that can be added before a plastic hinge is formed at mid-span be $W_2$, then the additional mid-span moment due to this load is that for a simply-supported beam and equals $W_2 L/8$.

$$\text{Total mid-span moment} = \frac{W_1 L}{24} + \frac{W_2 L}{8} \tag{5.VIII}$$

Since a plastic hinge is now formed at mid-span:

$$M_p = \frac{W_1 L}{24} + \frac{W_2 L}{8} \tag{5.IX}$$

Combining equations (5.VIII) and (5.VII) we get:

$$\frac{W_1 L}{24} + \frac{W_2 L}{8} = \frac{W_1 L}{12}$$

$$\frac{W_2 L}{8} = \frac{W_1 L}{24} \tag{5.X}$$

Therefore $W_1 = 3W_2$

Total collapse load $= \gamma_f W = W_1 + W_2$

$$\text{or } W_2 = \gamma_f W - W_1 \tag{5.XI}$$

Introducing equation (5.XI) to equation (5.X):

$$W_1 = 3(\gamma_f W - W_1) = 3\gamma_f W - 3W_1$$

$$4W_1 = 3\gamma_f W \tag{5.XII}$$

$$W_1 = \frac{3\gamma_f W}{4}$$

Substituting equation (5.XII) into equation (5.VII):

$$M_p = \frac{\frac{3}{4}\gamma_f WL}{12} = \gamma_f \frac{WL}{16} \tag{5.XIII}$$

The same result may be obtained by using virtual work equations, i.e. by equating the work done by the loads to the work absorbed in the hinges for some small displacement.

Let rotation of one end of the beam be some small arbitrary angle $\theta$; then rotation at the centre hinge is $2\theta$. The vertical distance at the centre hinge is

$$\frac{L}{2}\theta \quad \text{(see Fig. 5.15)}$$

Work done in hinges $= M_p \theta + M_p 2\theta + M_p \theta = 4 M_p \theta$

Work done by load $= \gamma_f W \frac{1}{2}\frac{L}{2}\theta = \frac{1}{4}\gamma_f WL\theta$

The uniform load moves through an average distance of $\frac{1}{2}\frac{L\theta}{2}$.

$$4 M_p \theta = \frac{\gamma_f WL\theta}{4}$$

At collapse:

$$M_p = \gamma_f \frac{WL}{16}$$

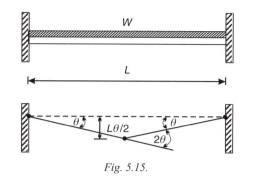

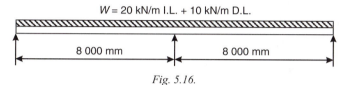

*Fig. 5.15.*

W = 20 kN/m I.L. + 10 kN/m D.L.

| 8 000 mm | 8 000 mm |

*Fig. 5.16.*

*Example 5.8.1. The spans and loadings of a two-span beam are shown in Fig. 5.16. Select a suitable UB in grade S 275 steel, (i) using elastic design procedures, (ii) using plastic design.*

## SOLUTION

| IL | $= 20 \times 1.6$ | $= 32 \text{ kN/m}$ | 256 kN per span |
|---|---|---|---|
| DL | $= 10 \times 1.4$ | $= 14 \text{ kN/m}$ | 112 kN per span |
| Total load | | $= 46 \text{ kN/m}$ | 368 kN per span |

### (i) Using elastic analysis

The maximum bending moment at the centre support is

$$\frac{368 \times 8}{8} = 368 \text{ kNm}$$

$$\text{Shear} = \frac{368}{2} + \frac{368}{8} = 230 \text{ kN}$$

Using elastic design and assigning a stress of 275 N/mm² for grade S 275 steel, the minimum plastic modulus required:

$$\frac{368 \times 10^3}{275} = 1338 \text{ cm}^3$$

There are three sections with equal mass that can be selected. These are:

$$406 \times 178 \times 67 \text{ UB}, \ S_x = 1\,346 \text{ cm}^3$$

$$457 \times 152 \times 67 \text{ UB}, \ S_x = 1\,453 \text{ cm}^3$$

$$457 \times 191 \times 67 \text{ UB}, \ S_x = 1\,471 \text{ cm}^3$$

Other factors being equal, the last section, i.e. $457 \times 191 \times 67$ UB, with the highest values for $S_x$ and $I$ will be the preferred choice. This section, then, will be selected for the checks that will follow.

Properties of trial section:

$$S_x = 1\,471 \text{ cm}^3, \ T = 12.7 \text{ mm} \ \therefore p = 275 \text{ N/mm}^2$$

$$D = 453.4 \text{ mm}, \ t = 8.5 \text{ mm}$$

$$\text{Shear capacity of the section} = \frac{0.6 \times 275 \times 453.4 \times 8.5}{1\,000}$$

$$= 636.0 \text{ kN}$$

The applied shear (230 kN) is less than $0.6 \times$ shear capacity:

$$0.6 \times 636 = 381.6 \text{ kN}$$

No reduction in moment capacity is required.

This is greater than the applied maximum moment of 368 kNm, therefore the section is satisfactory.

## (ii) Using plastic analysis

In any structure during loading the first plastic hinge will form when the elastic ratio of the applied moment/plastic moment capacity at any point reaches unity. Subsequent hinges will form as this ratio reaches unity at different points in the frame. In the case of a two span beam with a constant section, the first hinge will form at the central support; subsequent hinges will then be formed towards the outside supports in the spans. Thus there will be a load when the support just becomes plastic; as the load is increased passed this point, then the span hinges will also be formed and the whole system will turn into a mechanism.

The maximum bending moment is given by the following formulae:

$$M_p = \frac{W_{col}L^2}{11.66} \left( \text{or } M_p = 0.686 \frac{W_{col}L^2}{8} \right)$$

$$M_{p \ (required)} = \frac{46 \times 8^2}{11.66} = 252.5 \text{ kNm}$$

Plastic modulus required:

$$S_{p\,(required)} = \frac{252.5 \times 10^3}{275} = 918.2 \text{ cm}^3$$

The lightest section to fill this requirement is a 457 × 152 × 52 UB ($S_x = 1\,096$ cm³)

$$T = 10.9 \text{ mm} \therefore p_y = 275 \text{ N/mm}^2$$

$$D = 449.8 \text{ mm}, \quad t = 7.6 \text{ mm}$$

$$r_y = 31.1 \text{ mm}$$

Shear capacity:

$$0.6 \times 275 \times 449.8 \times \frac{7.6}{10^3} = 564.0 \text{ kN}$$

Maximum shear at support:

$$F_v = \frac{252.5}{8} + \frac{368}{2} = 215.6 \text{ kN}$$

By inspection, this is less than 0.6 of the shear capacity (338.4 kN) of the section, therefore there will be no need to reduce the moment capacity of the section for shear.

$$\text{Moment capacity} = 275 \times \frac{1094}{10^3} = 301 \text{ kNm}$$

Both flanges must be restrained at hinge positions and at a point located at a maximum distance, $L_u$, from the hinge position (§5.3.3).
    In this case:

$$L_u = \frac{38 \times 3.11 \times 10}{\left[ \dfrac{0}{130} + \left( \dfrac{275}{275} \right)^2 \left( \dfrac{43.9}{36} \right)^2 \right]^{0.5}} = 969 \text{ mm}$$

Under §5.2.3.7, stiffeners must be provided at the supports if the shear is greater than 10 per cent of the shear capacity of the section. Since by inspection this occurs in this case, stiffeners must be provided at the central support.
    A comparison of the section masses with the two designs gives an insight into the relative economy of the methods. Although it must be understood that the solution with the lightest section may not always be the least expensive, especially if more work, such as providing bracing and stiffeners, has to be carried out on the material, the comparative masses per metre are:

| | |
|---|---|
| Simple elastic design | 67 kg |
| Plastic design | 52 kg |

The cost of providing extra restraints and stiffeners for the plastic design must also be taken into account when comparing the two designs.

# 6. Beams

## 6.1. Conditions of equilibrium

Part of structural design, including most of the simpler problems, is performed with the aid of statics alone. Structures which can be solved purely by applying the conditions of static equilibrium are called statically determinate or isostatic structures. Those which cannot be solved by statics alone, are called *statically indeterminate* or *hyperstatic* structures.

Forces can be resolved into two components at right angles. In practice, it is convenient to choose the horizontal and vertical as the two directions. Verticality is, by definition, the direction of gravitational forces, and the majority of forces acting on the structure, i.e. dead load and imposed load, act vertically. Most of the remaining forces act horizontally, i.e. wind forces, water and soil pressure, all acting on a vertical plane.

To determine whether or not a structure is in equilibrium, the forces acting upon it must be resolved both vertically and horizontally. If the vertical components of the forces do not balance, the residual vertical force will cause the structure to move along a vertical path with accelerating speed. If the horizontal components of the force do not balance the structure will accelerate along a horizontal path in the direction of the residual horizontal force.

But while the equilibrium of vertical and horizontal forces ensure that a structure does not move bodily, it does not determine whether or not the structure would rotate under the action of the same system of vertical and horizontal forces. For example, the structure shown in Fig. 6.1 satisfies the equilibrium of vertical and horizontal forces, but it will obviously rotate about a pivot O, because of a lack of equilibrium of moments.

Consequently, three conditions need to be fulfilled for a planar body under a system of coplanar forces to remain in equilibrium:

The algebraic sum of all vertical forces is zero ($\Sigma V = 0$)
The algebraic sum of all horizontal forces is zero ($\Sigma H = 0$)
The algebraic sum of all moments about some axis is zero ($\Sigma M = 0$)

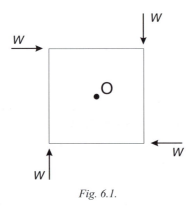

*Fig. 6.1.*

Note: For those who like to use mnemonic signs and phrases:

1. all up = all down

2. all in = all out

3. taking moments

## 6.2. Shear force

The shear force at any section of a beam is the resultant vertical force acting at the section due to the action of all external forces normal to the longitudinal axis of the beam, on either the left or right of the section.

It is usual to consider the shear force positive if the resultant forces tending to shear the beam on each side of a section form a clockwise couple; if an anticlockwise couple is formed, the shear force is negative.

A shear force diagram shows graphically the variation of shear force along the length of a beam. Usually, positive shear forces are drawn above the base line, and negative shear forces below it.

The shear force diagram (SFD) for a statically determinate beam may be drawn as follows:

- Find beam reactions by taking moments about one reaction.
- Start at either support and calculate the shear force at each point load. Plot these values on the diagram and join the points with straight lines.

Points to remember when drawing shear force diagrams are:

- When a beam carries only concentrated point loads, the shear force is constant between these point loads.

- When a beam carries a distributed load, the shear force is not constant, and the shear force varies at a rate proportional to the load per unit length of the beam.
- The maximum shear force for a simply supported beam or cantilever is always at a support.

Note: A simply-supported beam is a beam which has only two supports on which it merely rests, i.e. the ends are not rigidly constrained at these points but can rotate freely when loads are applied.

A cantilever is a beam that is supported at one end only. This end must be 'built-in', either by actually building a short length into concrete etc. or securely fixing it to a rigid structure.

SFDs for some common types of beams are given in Appendix A.

## 6.3. Bending moment

The bending moment at any section of a beam is the resultant moment, about that section, of all the external forces acting either to the left or right of the section.

It is usual to consider a sagging moment as positive and a hogging moment as negative.

A bending moment diagram (BMD) shows graphically the distribution of bending moment along the length of a beam. Usually, positive bending moments are drawn above the base line and negative moments below it. However, some books and BS 5950 now introduce the convention that the bending moments are drawn, even for beams, below the base line on the tension side.

Note: As far as the authors are concerned, it does not matter whether the bending moment is drawn above or below the base line, provided the engineer is consistent and knows what he is doing.

The BMD for a statically determinate beam may be drawn as follows:

- Find beam reactions.
- Start at either end of a beam, or in the case of a cantilever start at the free end, and calculate the bending moment at each load point. Plot these values on the diagram and join the points with straight lines.
- In the case of distributed loads, bending moments are calculated at a number of points and the values joined by a smooth curve. Under a uniformly distributed load, the bending moment diagram is parabolic.

A point to remember when drawing the BMDs is that the bending moment is a maximum when the shear force is zero. Therefore, if a beam is loaded with point loads only, the maximum moment occurs at a point load, i.e. where the shear force diagram crosses the base line.

BMDs for some common types of beams are given in Appendix A.

## 6.4. Theory of simple bending

Having calculated the bending moment at any section of a beam, the next step in the design of beams is to determine the adequacy of the bending stresses of the section. This is done by applying the theory of simple bending.

However, the deduction of the correct analytical method was far from simple, since the distribution of stress and strain in beams is not uniform, and it took several centuries to obtain the correct solution.

Leonardo da Vinci first tackled the problem in the fifteenth century, but it was Galileo Galilei who proposed a solution in 1638, though this was incorrect.

Jacob Bernoulli (1654 – 1705) introduced the assumption that under a uniform bending moment, plane sections remain plane after bending.

Charles Augustin Coulomb (1736 – 1800) gave the first correct solution to the problem in 1773, when he obtained the true relationship between the applied load, the bending moment, moment of resistance, and shear force.

However, it was Louis Marie Navier's simpler method, published in 1826, that has become generally accepted. In this, Bernoulli's assumption is followed, i.e. plane sections remain plane after bending. Under the action of a uniform moment, $M$, two originally straight and parallel planes AB and CD remain straight, but rotate around a common centre of curvature, O (see Fig. 6.2). The upper fibres, nearer to O, are in compression, whilst the lower fibres, furthest from O, are in tension. There is an intermediate layer, which will neither be compressed nor stretched. This layer, NS, which does not alter in length, is called the *neutral surface*, and its intersection with a transverse section is called the *neutral axis* (NA). The bending stress at the neutral axis is then always zero. Fibres further away from the NA have a higher stress than those nearer to the NA.

In deriving the formula for simple bending, the following assumptions are made:

- The beam is straight before bending and uniform in section.
- Plane transverse sections remain plane after bending.
- The material is homogeneous and remains elastic, i.e. obeys Hooke's Law.
- The Modulus of Elasticity or Young's Modulus is assumed to have the same value in compression as in tension.

- Longitudinal layers of the material are free from interaction among each other, and consequently act as if they were separated from adjacent layers.
- Longitudinal layers of the beam bend into circular arcs around a centre of curvature, and the radius of curvature is large compared with the sectional dimensions and the length of the beam.
- The transverse section of the beam is symmetrical about an axis through its centroid in the plane of bending, i.e. about axis Y–Y in Fig. 6.2.

In order to simplify the derivation of the formula for simple bending, let us assume that the neutral axis passes halfway through the beam (see Fig. 6.2).

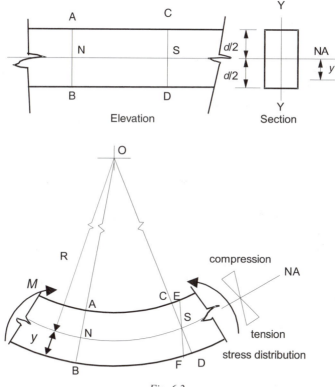

*Fig. 6.2.*

Now draw a line EF through S parallel to AB. CE represents the change of length of the extreme fibre in compression and FD represents the change of length of the extreme fibre in tension.

There is no change of length of the neutral surface NS. Let $e$ be the change of length in tension over the original length:

$$e = \frac{FD}{BF} = \frac{FD}{NS}$$

(6.I)

Since $BF = NS$

Let $R$ be the radius of curvature, measured to the neutral surface, and $y$ be the distance from the neutral surface to the extreme fibres of the beam, in this case to the underside of the beam.

The sides of the triangle FSD and NOS are parallel and therefore:

$$\frac{FD}{NS} = \frac{SF}{ON}$$

(6.II)

Since $e = \dfrac{FD}{NS}$ and $\dfrac{SF}{ON} = \dfrac{y}{R}$, equation (6.II) becomes

$$e = \frac{y}{R}$$

(6.III)

Since $f = E \times e$

(6.IV)

Substituting equation (6.III) into equation (6.IV):

$$f = \frac{Ey}{R}$$

(6.V)

Equation (6.V) states that the stress varies directly as the distance $y$, as shown in Fig. 6.2.

Rearranging equation (6.V):

$$\frac{f}{y} = \frac{E}{R}$$

(6.VI)

The force acting on an infinitesimally small area $(dA)$ at a distance $y$ from the neutral axis is:

$$dF = f \times dA$$

(6.VII)

The moment of the force about the neutral axis is:

$$dM = y \cdot dF = yf \cdot dA = y\frac{Ey}{R} \cdot dA$$

(6.VIII)

$$\text{or} \quad dM = \frac{Ey^2}{R} \cdot dA$$

The total moment of resistance, $M$, of the section is the sum of all the infinitesimally small elements, $dM$, which is expressed mathematically in the following form:

$$M = \int \frac{Ey^2}{R} \cdot dA \qquad (6.IX)$$

The Modulus of Elasticity ($E$) is constant, and the radius of curvature ($R$) is independent of the depth, $y$, therefore $E$ and $R$ can be taken outside the integral sign:

$$M = \frac{E}{R} \int y^2 \cdot dA \qquad (6.X)$$

$\int y^2 \cdot dA$ is called the *second moment of area* and is denoted by $I$. This is a purely geometric property of the section and is independent of the type of material used. $I$ is frequently called the *moment of inertia*, since the same $I$ occurs in dynamic calculations, but strictly speaking the term *second moment of area* is the more correct one. However, both terms are equally acceptable in practice.

Equation (6.X) now becomes:

$$M = \frac{E}{R} \times I \qquad (6.XI)$$

Rearranging equation (6.XI), we get:

$$\frac{M}{I} = \frac{E}{R} \qquad (6.XII)$$

The formula for simple bending as presented by Navier's theorem can now be given its usual form, by combining equations (6.VI) and (6.XII).

$$\frac{f}{y} = \frac{E}{R} = \frac{M}{I} \qquad (6.XIII)$$

where:

$f$ = the stress in any layer
$y$ = the distance of the layer under stress from the Neutral Axis
$E$ = the Modulus of Elasticity or Young's Modulus
$R$ = the local radius of curvature of the beam
$M$ = the maximum bending moment, which must be equal to or less than the moment of resistance of the beam section
$I$ = the second moment of area or the moment of inertia of the cross-section of the beam.

The formula for simple bending, i.e. equation (6.XIII), is an important one and is worth committing to memory; it may be remembered by combining the symbols into a single mnemonic word 'fyermi', with the odd letters (fem) forming the numerators of the equation.

The important part of this formula for the beam design is:

$$\frac{f}{y} = \frac{M}{I} \tag{6.XIV}$$

The formula is applied to the outside layer, usually referred to as the extreme fibre, where $f$ and $y$ have their maximum values. A slight rearrangement of equation (6.XIV) will give:

$$\frac{M}{f} = \frac{I}{y} \tag{6.XV}$$

The ratio $I/y$ in which both $I$ and $y$ represent geometrical properties of the beam section, is called the *Section Modulus* or the *Elastic Modulus of the Section* and is usually denoted by $Z$. Tables of properties of the principal steel sections in use appear in Appendices B, C and D at the end of this book; more detailed tables may be found in Volume 1 of the guide to BS 5950.

With the introduction of the section modulus ($Z$), equation (6.XV) becomes:

$$\frac{M}{f} = Z \text{ or } M = fZ \tag{6.XVI}$$

So, it can be seen, that if the necessary value of $Z$ is known, a suitable section to resist the maximum bending moment may be selected from the tables.

When a beam is subjected to bending, the bending stresses vary from zero at the centre to a maximum at the extreme fibres. Most of the cross-sectional area of the material of an I-beam is located in its flanges, the most highly stressed zones, which are further from the NA. Therefore, the I-beam is better able to resist bending than a rectangular beam.

When an I-section is used as a beam, it is assumed, conservatively, that its flanges resist the bending moment, while its web is resisting the shear force.

## 6.5. Ultimate load capacity

The above explanation describes the behaviour of a beam within elastic limits, i.e. until yield is reached at the extreme fibres. It has been found that the attainment of yield at extreme fibres need not represent the ultimate load capacity of the section. An examination of Figs. 2.1 and 2.2 shows that when the yield has been reached, the material will tend to strain at constant stress. During this straining, the section will carry further load until the stress across the whole section has reached yield. At this point, there will be an increase in deflection with little or no increase in load; this point in the loading pattern represents failure.

This behaviour of the beam section has been the basis of plastic design (see Chapter 5). It also provides a method of determining the ultimate capacity of the section.

In considering limit states, especially that of strength, failure will be considered when the structure reaches the load at which deflections increase with no change of load. Clearly then, the ultimate capacity of a beam will be reached when plasticity has taken place over the whole section. This leads to the fundamental design consideration that the plastic moment capacity is the limiting value at failure. In order to ensure that there is no permanent straining on the extreme fibre, which could cause either a bent beam appearance or affect finishes, the maximum moment is limited to the elastic value at working loads.

This limitation is a serviceability control because it will not relate to the failure of the structure. The maximum moment is limited to 1.2 times the elastic moment capacity, based on the elastic section modulus for rolled sections for simply supported beams and cantilevers. The choice of 1.2 is based on the lowest factor of safety used in normal design.

## 6.6. Simple beam design

When designing a simply supported beam carrying a uniformly distributed load (UDL), it is necessary to keep the ultimate capacity greater than the factored applied load and the deflection within the limiting values. The procedure followed in checking the adequacy of the beam is:

- *Ultimate moment capacity.* This is calculated from the plastic modulus of the section ($S$) and the design strength ($p_y$). It must not exceed the applied moment. (If the section is not a rolled section there may be other considerations that also need be taken into account.)
- *Shear capacity.* This is the product of the shear strength ($0.6p_y$) times the shear area, i.e. $Dt$ (depth of section by web thickness).
- *Deflection.* The elastic deflection of the beam using the unfactored imposed load is calculated in this check. This should not exceed span/360 if there are brittle finishes, such as plaster, or span/200 in other cases. There are, however, cases where other values are more appropriate; it is the engineer's responsibility to ensure that such situ-

ations are recognised. (Deflection formulae for some common types of beam loading are given in Appendix A.)

- *Lateral torsional buckling.* This form of failure, i.e. the beam deflecting sideways and twisting under vertical load, may be prevented by tying to the compression flange *in situ* or pre cast concrete floors.
- *Web buckling.* The web of an I-beam may be considered as a strut which will buckle at a critical load. This will occur at points of concentrated load or at supports.
- *Web crushing or bearing.* The web of an I-beam may be crushed in bearing at its junction with the flange. This will occur at points of concentrated load or at supports.

In the elementary Example 6.6.1, it will be assumed that bearing and buckling of the web will not be critical. It will be found from experience that these modes of failure will generally occur only when a very short span carries a heavy load or where a heavy concentrated point load occurs adjacent to a support.

Step by step calculations in simple beam design are:

| | |
|---|---|
| Step 1 | Determine the loading conditions and factored loads |
| Step 2 | Sketch the beam and loading |
| Step 3 | Compute the maximum bending moment |
| Step 4 | Find the required plastic modulus |
| Step 5 | Select a suitable section |
| Step 6 | Check for beam weight |
| Step 7 | Compute the maximum shear force |
| Step 8 | Find the maximum average shear stress |
| Step 9 | Find the imposed load deflection |
| Step 10 | Find the maximum allowed deflection |
| Step 11 | Ensure restraint is provided to the compression flange |
| Step 12 | Check for web buckling at the supports or point loads |
| Step 13 | Check for web bearing at supports or point loads |

Steps 1 to 6 inclusive refer to bending moment capacity (flanges).

Steps 7 and 8 refer to shear capacity (web).

Steps 9 and 10 refer to excessive deflection.

Step 11 refers to lateral torsional buckling.

Steps 12 and 13 apply when a load or reaction is applied to the flange of a section.

*Example 6.6.1. A simply supported beam, of 5 m span, carries a reinforced concrete floor capable of providing lateral restraint to the top compression flange. The uniformly distributed load is made up of 20 kN/m imposed load plus 20 kN/m dead load. Choose a suitable I-section beam using S 275 steel. It may be assumed that the section is held on web cleats and that web bearing and buckling are not critical.*

## SOLUTION

Step 1     The factored loads are:

| | | | | |
|---|---|---|---|---|
| Imposed load | = | 20 × 1.6 | = | 32.0 kN/m |
| Dead load | = | 20 × 1.4 | = | 28.0 kN/m |
| Total load | | | = | 60.0 kN/m |

Step 2

60 kN/m

5 m

Step 3     Maximum bending moment $= \dfrac{WL^2}{8}$

$$= \frac{60 \times 5^2}{8}$$

$$= 187.5 \text{ kNm}$$

Step 4     Plastic modulus required $= M/p_y$

$$\frac{187.5 \times 10^3}{275} = 682 \text{ cm}^3$$

$$\therefore S_{x \text{ (required)}} = 682 \text{ cm}^3$$

Step 5    The choice is between the following sections:
$305 \times 127 \times 48$ UB ($S_x = 711$ cm$^3$)
$305 \times 165 \times 46$ UB ($S_x = 720$ cm$^3$), and
$356 \times 171 \times 45$ UB ($S_x = 775$ cm$^3$)
The deeper beam is lighter and more efficient in carrying the bending moment and would normally be the first choice. It is important, however, to remember that the engineer's choice may also be affected by the available space. In many structures there is a tight limit on the headroom and the storey height, which may dictate the adoption of a shallower beam section.

Step 6    The weight of the beam is approximately 0.450 kN/m.
New trial factored load

$$= 60 + (0.45 \times 1.4) = 60.63 \text{ kN/m}$$

$$\text{Maximum BM} = \frac{60.63 \times 5^2}{8} = 189.5 \text{ kNm}$$

$$S_{x(\text{required})} = \frac{189.5 \times 10^3}{275} = 689 \text{ cm}^3$$

$S_{x(\text{required})}$ is less than $S_{x(\text{provided})}$, therefore the chosen UB is satisfactory.

Step 7

$$\text{Maximum shear force} = \frac{60.63 \times 5}{2} = 151.60 \text{ kN}$$

Step 8

$$\text{Average shear stress} = \frac{151.6 \times 10^3}{351.4 \times 7.0} = 61.6 \text{ N/mm}^2$$

This shear stress is well within the allowable

$$(0.6 \times 275) = 165 \text{ N/mm}^2.$$

In practice, shear stress is seldom critical. It may, however, become so when a very short span carries a heavy load, or when carrying a heavy concentrated point load near a support.

Step 9          The assessment of the structure's behaviour for deflection is
                a matter of engineering judgement. Rules covering deflec-
                tion in some common situations are given in §2.5.2 but it
                points out that these limits may be varied at the engineer's
                discretion to fit circumstances. For this example, it will be
                assumed that the maximum deflection for the imposed load
                is span/360 at working load.

$$Deflection\ \delta = \frac{5}{384} \times \frac{WL^3}{EI}$$

$$= \frac{5}{384} \times \frac{\left(20 \times 5 \times 1\,000\right) \times \left(5\,000\right)^3}{205\,000 \times 120\,700\,000}$$

$$= 6.58\ \text{mm}$$

Step 10         Recommended maximum deflection:

$$\frac{5\,000}{360} = 13.88\ \text{mm}$$

                Therefore the deflection of the beam is well within the
                allowable.

Step 11         Restraint is provided by the floor and no further check is
                required.

Steps 12        The beam is assumed to be supported on web cleats; web
and 13          bearing and buckling are not, therefore, design criteria.

*Example 6.6.2. A simply-supported beam, of 7 m span, carries a reinforced
concrete floor capable of providing lateral restraint to the top compression
flange. The total UDL is made up of 100 kN dead load, including self-weight
plus 150 kN imposed load. In addition the beam carries a point load (PL) at
midspan made up of 50 kN dead load and 50 kN imposed load. Choose a
suitable Universal Beam using S 275 steel. (Also carry out the web buckling
and web bearing checks, assuming a stiff bearing length of 75 mm.)*

SOLUTION

Step 1      Load factors $\gamma_f$:

            DL  =  1.4
            IL  =  1.6                              (§2.4.1)

Factored loads:
UDL

$$\underset{140}{\left(100 \times 1.4\right)} \quad + \quad \underset{240}{\left(150 \times 1.6\right)} \quad = \quad 380 \text{ kN}$$

PL

$$\underset{70}{\left(50 \times 1.4\right)} \quad + \quad \underset{80}{\left(50 \times 1.6\right)} \quad = \quad 150 \text{ kN}$$

Step 2

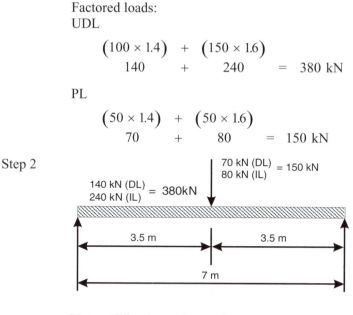

Note: All loads are factored

Step 3    Maximum BM:

$$M_x = \frac{380 \times 7}{8} + \frac{150 \times 7}{4} = 595 \text{ kNm}$$

Step 4    $S_{x \text{ (required)}} = M_x / p_y$

$$\frac{595 \times 10^3}{275} = 2\,164.0 \text{ cm}^3$$

Step 5    Choose a 533 × 210 × 92 UB ($S_x = 2\,360 \text{ cm}^3$)
Section properties:

$D = 533.1$ mm,              $B = 209.3$ mm

$d = 476.5$ mm,              $b = \dfrac{1}{2} B = 104.7$ mm

$T = 15.6$ mm                $I_x = 55\,230 \text{ cm}^4$

$t = 10.1$ mm                $Z_x = 2072 \text{ cm}^3$

Check design strength $p_y$:

$$T = 15.6 < 16 \text{ mm}$$

$$\therefore p_y = 275 \text{ N/mm}^2$$

Check outstanding element of compression flange:

$$\frac{b}{T} = \frac{104.7}{15.6} = 6.7 < 9\,\varepsilon$$

(Table 11)

Check web with NA mid-depth:

$$\frac{d}{t} = \frac{476.5}{10.2} = 46.7 < 80\,\varepsilon$$

Since $p_y = 275 \text{ N/mm}^2$, $\varepsilon = 1.0$

Section is plastic. Note that a compact section would be sufficient as there is no plastic redistribution of moment.

Step 6   $S_x$ will still be satisfactory taking self-weight into consideration

Step 7   Factored shear force:

$$F_v \text{ (at supports)} = \frac{(380 + 150)}{2} = 265 \text{ kN}$$

Step 8   Shear area:

$$A_v = tD = 10.1 \times 533.1 = 5\,384 \text{ mm}^2$$

Shear capacity:

$$P_v = 0.6\,p_y\,A_v$$
$$= \frac{0.6 \times 275 \times 5\,384}{10^3}$$
$$= 888 \text{ kN} > F_v$$

$\therefore$ the value is satisfactory.

Check moment capacity $M_c$:
Factored shear force $F_v$ (at maximum moment) = 75 kN.
Since $F_v = 75 < 0.6\,P_v$, shear force is 'low'.
$M_c = p_y\,S_x = 275 \times 2\,366/10^3 = 651$ kNm

Note: To avoid irreversible deformation under serviceability loads, the value of $M_c$ should be limited to $1 \times 2p_y Z$ for simply-supported beams (§4.2.5).

Check:

$$1.2\,p_y\,Z_x = 1.2 \times 275 \times 2\,072/10^3 = 651 \text{ kNm}$$

The lesser of the two values for $M_c$ is 651 kNm.

Since $M_c = 651$ kNm $> M_x = 595$ kNm
the value is satisfactory.

Step 9    Serviceability loads (unfactored imposed loads):

$P = 50$ kN $W = 150$ kN

$$\text{Actual deflection, } \delta = \frac{L^3}{EI}\left[\frac{P}{48} + \frac{5W}{384}\right]$$

$$= \frac{(7 \times 1\,000)^3}{205\,000 \times 55\,230 \times 10}\left[\frac{50}{48} + \frac{5 \times 150}{384}\right]$$

$$= 9.10 \text{ mm}$$

Step 10    $$\text{Allowable deflection} = \frac{L}{360}$$

$$= \frac{7\,000}{360}$$

$$= 19 \text{ mm}$$

∴ deflection is satisfactory.

Step 11    The check for lateral torsional buckling is satisfied, since the reinforced concrete floor provided lateral restraint to the compression flange.

Step 12    Check for web bearing:

Bearing capacity $(P_{bw}) = (b_1 + nk)\, tp_{yw}$     (§4.5.2.1)

Where:

$p_{yw}$ = design strength of web = 275 N/mm$^2$
$b_1$ = stiff bearing length = 75 mm
$n = 2$ as the stiff bearing is at the end of the beam
$k = T + r$ = flange thickness + root radius = 15.6 + 12.7
    = 28.3 mm.

Bearing capacity:

$$(P_{bw}) = \frac{(75 + 2 \times 28.3) \times 10.1 \times 275}{1\,000} = 366 \text{ kN}$$

366 kN > 265 kN
∴ the value is satisfactory.

Step 13    Check for web buckling:
Buckling resistance:

$$P_x = \frac{a_e + 0.7d}{1.4d} \times \frac{25\varepsilon t}{\sqrt{(b_1 + nk)d}} \times P_{bw} \quad (§4.5.3.1)$$

Where:
stiff bearing length, $b_1$ = 75 mm
$a_e$ = distance to load or reaction to the nearer end of the member, in this case 37.5 mm

$\varepsilon$ = square root of ratio of stresses
    $= \sqrt{275/p_y} = \sqrt{275/275} = 1.0$

$d$ = depth of the section web
$t$ = thickness of web
$b_1$ = stiff bearing length
$n = 2$ as the support is at the end of the beam
$k$ = thickness of flange (+ root radius for a rolled section)
$P_{bw}$ = web bearing capacity as given above

$$P_x = \frac{37.5 + (0.7 \times 476.5)}{1.4 \times 476.5} \times \frac{25 \times 1 \times 10.1}{\sqrt{(75 + 2 \times 28.3) \times 476.5}} \times 366$$

    = 206 kN

$P_x$ = 206 kN < 265 kN
∴ stiffeners will be required.

## Design of stiffeners

The stiffeners are normally welded one each side of the web as shown in Fig. 6.3.

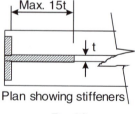

Plan showing stiffeners

*Fig. 6.3.*

Part of the web, not exceeding fifteen times its thickness, may also be included in the design. Stiffener thickness should be at least 6 mm; for a heavy section thicker plate should be employed. Stiffeners are normally welded to the web and compression flange; if they are welded to the tension flange then care must be exercised to ensure that there is no risk of brittle fracture or fatigue. At the end of the beam this is not normally a problem because the moment is zero and there is no tension stress, unless the beam is continuous.

Assume that two stiffeners 6 mm × 75 mm are welded as shown in the plan (see Fig. 6.3), then the buckling resistance may be determined as follows:

Area of the stiffeners and attached web =

$$2 \times 6 \times 75 + \left(10.1 \times 15 + 6\right) \times 10.1 = 900 + 1591$$

$$= 2\,491 \text{ mm}^2$$

$$= 24.91 \text{ cm}^2$$

$$I \text{ of the stiffeners} = \frac{160.1^3 \times 6}{12 \times 10\,000} = 205 \text{ cm}^4$$

Radius of gyration ($r$) of the stiffeners =

$$\sqrt{\frac{I}{A}} = \sqrt{\frac{205}{24.91}} = 2.87 \text{ cm}$$

It is assumed that the flanges are restrained against rotation so the length is taken as 0.7 × the depth of the web, $d$.

The value of the slenderness ratio, $\lambda = \dfrac{0.7 \times 476.5}{2.87 \times 10} = 11.6$

The value of $p_c = 275$ N/mm², taken from Table 24(c).

The buckling resistance of the web stiffeners

$$= \frac{275 \times 2\,491}{10^3} = 685 \text{ kN}$$

It will often be found that once stiffeners are provided then they will, generally, be more than adequate for the requirements.

## 6.7. Local buckling

All types of plate elements under compression associated with axial force, bending or shear will carry a certain load and then deform out of shape and buckle with a consequent loss in strength. This behaviour has been recognised over a number of years in certain design areas, notably cold-formed steel sections and aluminium. There are occasions where similar behaviour is observed in hot-finished sections, particularly with thin flanges and webs where the $d/t$ ratio is high. In such cases the designer must allow for the reduction in strength.

The rules in BS 5950 are framed in such a way that the engineer can assess the carrying capacity in various situations and determine where local buckling can occur. In order to carry out this task sections have been grouped into four classes, see §3.5.2:

- *Class 1.* Plastic cross-sections are those in which all elements subject to compression have plastic hinge rotation capacity and these will comply with the values given in Tables 11 and 12 for plastic elements. A plastic hinge can be developed with sufficient rotation capacity to allow redistribution of moments within the structure.

  Only class 1 sections may be used for plastic analysis and design.

- *Class 2.* Compact cross-sections are those in which all elements subject to compression comply with the values given in Tables 11 and 12 for compact elements. The full plastic moment capacity can be developed but local buckling may prevent development of a plastic hinge with sufficient rotation capacity to permit plastic analysis and design.

  Class 2 sections can be used without restriction except for plastic analysis and design.

- *Class 3.* Semi-compact sections are those in which all elements subject to compression comply with the values given in Tables 11 and 12 for semi-compact elements. The stress at the extreme fibres can reach the design strength but local buckling may prevent the development of the full plastic moment.

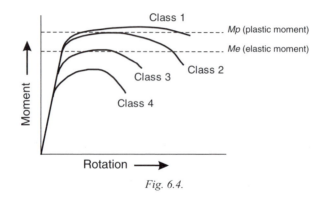

*Fig. 6.4.*

- *Class 4.* Slender sections are those that contain slender elements subject to compression due to moment or axial load.

Local buckling may prevent the stress in a slender section from reaching the design strength.

Design of class 4 sections is considered in §3.6.

The above definitions, based on BS 5950 (§3.5.2), give a basic description of the various types of section, and Tables 11 and 12 give the limiting values. An element is generally taken as the web or flange of the section although it may be any other plate in a member, i.e. a stiffener (which is governed by separate rules).

The practical effect of this may be seen in Fig. 6.4 where moment/rotation curves are drawn for sections of each classification, assuming the flanges are the critical feature.

From this, it will be seen that plastic sections (class 1) have a long plateau where rotation takes place at or just above the theoretical value of $M_p$ (plastic moment capacity). Compact sections (class 2) will reach the value of $M_p$ but will then start to lose strength if an attempt to rotate is made. Semi-compact sections (class 3) will start to buckle and lose strength once yield has been reached on the extreme fibres (elastic limit). Class 4 sections (slender cross-sections) will buckle locally before their elastic capacity is reached, forming the type of failure exhibited by cold-formed sections. Part 1 of BS 5950 gives estimates of the capacity of this class of section similar to the detailed methods given in Part 5, which covers cold-formed sections.

In practical design terms, it will be necessary for engineers to keep a watch on their choice of sections to ensure that local buckling is not a design problem or that, if this does happen, due account is taken. As a general guide, local buckling will not be critical in the following cases:

- Universal beams and columns, joists, channels and hollow sections in simple bending.
- Stanchions using universal column sections.
- All members where tension dominates the design.

It will be seen from this list that many of the common structures may be designed without recourse to the local buckling rules. Plate girders and other fabricated sections must always be checked to ensure that the limits are not exceeded. Rolled sections which need checking include angles and universal beams when used as struts carrying dominant compression forces.

Design of various section classes depends on the behaviour in local buckling. Plastic and compact sections need no further checking or adjustment to their load capacities and may be taken to their full value. The sole limitations are that only plastic sections may be used at hinge locations in plastic analysis and design. However, there are restrictions on the calculated capacity of semi-compact and slender cross-sections.

BS 5950 has now adopted a limiting area reduction for slender (class 4) cross-sections in line with those adopted in the cold-formed section parts and the Eurocodes.

## 6.8. Laterally unrestrained beams

A beam, with no lateral restraint, subjected to loading, may move sideways and twist before failing at a load below that expected by simple bending theory. This mode of behaviour has been termed lateral torsional buckling because there is both lateral movement and twisting (see Fig. 6.5).

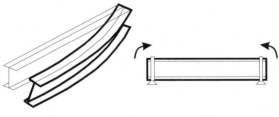

*Fig. 6.5.*

The design process of BS 5950 (§4.3) makes use of a number of section properties to enable the derivation of the capacity of a section to lateral torsional buckling. These properties are:

$r_y$ = radius of gyration about the vertical axis.
$u$ = a property related to the torsional strength of the section, buckling parameter.

*BS 5950  Table 18  Equivalent uniform moment factor $m_{LT}$ for lateral-torsional buckling*

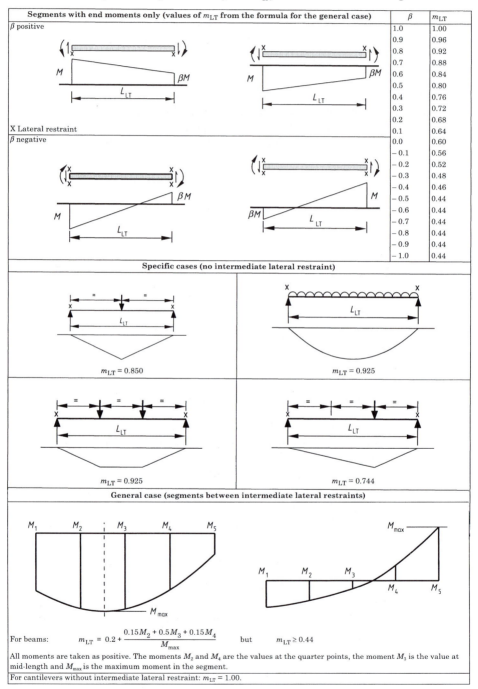

| | $\beta$ | $m_{LT}$ |
|---|---|---|
| | 1.0 | 1.00 |
| | 0.9 | 0.96 |
| | 0.8 | 0.92 |
| | 0.7 | 0.88 |
| | 0.6 | 0.84 |
| | 0.5 | 0.80 |
| | 0.4 | 0.76 |
| | 0.3 | 0.72 |
| | 0.2 | 0.68 |
| | 0.1 | 0.64 |
| | 0.0 | 0.60 |
| | $-0.1$ | 0.56 |
| | $-0.2$ | 0.52 |
| | $-0.3$ | 0.48 |
| | $-0.4$ | 0.46 |
| | $-0.5$ | 0.44 |
| | $-0.6$ | 0.44 |
| | $-0.7$ | 0.44 |
| | $-0.8$ | 0.44 |
| | $-0.9$ | 0.44 |
| | $-1.0$ | 0.44 |

For beams: $m_{LT} = 0.2 + \dfrac{0.15M_2 + 0.5M_3 + 0.15M_4}{M_{max}}$  but  $m_{LT} \geq 0.44$

All moments are taken as positive. The moments $M_2$ and $M_4$ are the values at the quarter points, the moment $M_3$ is the value at mid-length and $M_{max}$ is the maximum moment in the segment.

For cantilevers without intermediate lateral restraint: $m_{LT} = 1.00$.

$x$ = a property related to the warping strength of the section, torsional index.

$\beta_w$ = the ratio between the effective plastic modulus and the actual plastic modulus is 1.0 for class 1 and 2 sections. To be determined from §4.3.6.9 for class 3 and class 4 sections.

$S_x$ = the plastic modulus of the section.

It should be noted that hollow sections and beam shapes, bending about the weak axis, will not normally be subjected to this phenomenon and may be designed as restrained sections. Table 15 gives the limiting values for the slenderness ratio of rectangular sections where they are sufficiently stable to ensure that there is no lateral torsional buckling. Also all sections whose span is less than the critical length ($\lambda_{LT} < \lambda_{LO}$) will not be subject to this mode of failure.

The checking process, using BS 5950, on a section, selected by experience, and following on from the design of restrained beams, is as follows:

Step 14    Calculate the value of $\lambda$ ($L_E/r_y$)

Step 15    Adjust the value for the torsional and warping strength of the section.

The adjustment is carried out by calculating $\lambda_{LT}$, the equivalent slenderness, §4.3.6.7 where:

$$\lambda_{LT} = uv\lambda\sqrt{\beta_w}$$

The value of $u$ is taken directly from the section properties tables.

The value of slenderness factor, $v$, is obtained from Table 19 using the central column (flange ratio being 0.5) for equal flange sections.

Before this table can be used the value of $\lambda/x$ must be determined, where $x$ is another property of the section, which may be obtained from tables.

The value of $\beta_w$ is taken as 1.0 for class 1 and 2 cross-sections and see §4.3.6.9 for class 3 and 4 sections.

Step 16    The bending strength, $p_b$ (in N/mm$^2$), may then be taken from Table 16 or 17 using the calculated value of $\lambda_{LT}$.

Step 17    The buckling resistance moment, $M_b$, is then equal to $S_x p_b$ (i.e. $M_b = S_x p_b$) where $S_x$ is the plastic modulus of the section about the major axis.

This process enables the lateral torsional capacity of the section to be derived, but it takes no account of the shape of the bending moment diagram on the beam (moment gradient effect), e.g. different moments between restraints.

For this, an equivalent uniform moment, $m_{LT} M$, is calculated, and used to reduced the moment in a check against the moment capacity.

### Equivalent uniform moment

The equivalent uniform moment factor ($m_{LT}$) is calculated depending on the circumstances, using BS 5950 Table 18.

If the moment diagram is linear between the points of restraint then the value of $\beta$ is determined from the ratio of the moments at each end of the part of the beam. This is the ratio of the smaller end moment divided by the larger. It is important that the sign is correct. This will be positive if the moments produce tension on the same side of the member throughout its length. If there is a reversal of stress (double curvature bending) then the sign for $\beta$ will be negative. Thus the value of $\beta$ will be between $\pm 1$.

After calculating $m_{LT}$, the buckling resistance moment is multiplied by $m_{LT}$ to give the maximum moment resistance for lateral torsional buckling, or the actual maximum moment on the segment is reduced by $m_{LT}$. It should be noted that the value of $m_{LT}$ may be relatively small; it is, therefore, essential that the section is fully checked as a restrained beam.

*Example 6.8.1. As an example of an unrestrained beam, example 6.6.1 will be reworked assuming that the floor is incapable of providing restraint to the compression flange. The loading sketch and the maximum bending moment are all shown in example 6.6.1. This example may, therefore, start at Step 4, assuming a distributed load of 60 kN/m on a 5 m span giving a maximum moment of 187.50 kNm.*

### SOLUTION

Step 4    For the purposes of this example, it will be assumed that the beam is torsionally restrained and the compression flange is laterally restrained but free to rotate on plan at the supports. The effective length ($L_E$) in these circumstances is equal to $1.0L$ (BS 5950, Table 13). There are no intermediate restraints, so
$L_E = 5\ 000$ mm.

Step 14     The code gives no direct rules which may be used to calculate the section size when designing unrestrained beams. A satisfactory section seems to be a $457 \times 191 \times 67$ UB. This will now be checked in detail.

$r_y = 4.12$ cm

$$\lambda = \frac{L_E}{r_y} = \frac{5\,000}{4.12 \times 10} = 121.0$$

Step 15     $x = 37.9$

$$\frac{\lambda}{x} = \frac{121}{37.9} = 3.19$$

$v = 0.91$ from Table 19
$u = 0.872$ from section books
$m_{LT} = 0.925$ from Table 18
$\beta_w = 1.0$ for a class 1 or 2 cross-section
$\lambda_{LT} = uv\lambda\sqrt{\beta_w} = 0.872 \times 0.91 \times 121 \times 1.0 = 96$

Step 16     From Table 16, $p_b = 133$ N/mm$^2$

Step 17     $S_x = 1\,471$ cm$^3$

$$\text{Moment capacity} = \frac{133 \times 1\,471}{10^3} = 195.5 \text{ kNm}$$

This moment has now to be divided by $m_{LT}$ to give the buckling resistance moment, allowing for the moment gradient, giving:
$\frac{195.5}{0.925} = 211$ kNm, compared with the maximum moment of 187.5 kNm.

Alternatively, the maximum moment may be reduced by $m_{LT}$. This gives $187.5 \times 0.925 = 173.4$, compared with the moment capacity of 195.5.

The section is therefore satisfactory.

Step 18     The beam should be checked as a restrained beam for all the requirements as described in the text in Section 6.6.

## 6.9. Compound (plated) beams

### 6.9.1. Introduction

It is sometimes essential to increase the bending capacity or stiffness of a section by welding plates to the flanges. Such compound (plated) beams extend the range of the standard sections, especially when a shallow beam is required to gain headroom. The benefit of compounding is best shown by an example.

*Example 6.9.1. Steel beams having a clear span of 9.35 m are resting on 150 mm wide end bearings. The beams are spaced 3 m apart and carry a dead load of 5 kN/m², including an allowance for the weight of the section, and an imposed load of 15 kN/m². The maximum depth of the beam section is limited to 600 mm. Material to be used is of grade S 275 steel.*

### SOLUTION

Factoring the loads:

$$
\begin{array}{lll}
\text{Dead load} & = 5 \times 1.4 & = 7 \ \text{kN/m}^2 \\
\text{Imposed load} & = 15 \times 1.6 & = 24 \ \text{kN/m}^2 \\
\text{DL per metre} & = 7 \times 3 & = 21 \ \text{kN/m} \\
\text{IL per metre} & = 24 \times 3 & = 72 \ \text{kN/m} \\
\text{Total load} & = 93 \ \text{kN/m}
\end{array}
$$

The effective span is taken as the clear span plus half of the end bearing at each support.

$$
\begin{array}{lll}
\text{Effective span} & = & 9.35 + 2 \times 0.5 \times 0.150 = 9.50 \ \text{m} \\[4pt]
\text{Reactions} & = & \dfrac{93 \times 9.5}{2} = 442.0 \ \text{kN} \\[8pt]
\text{Moment} & = & \dfrac{93 \times 9.5^2}{8} = 1\,049.0 \ \text{kN} \\[8pt]
S \ \text{required} & = & \dfrac{1\,049 \times 10^6}{265 \times 10^3} = 3\,958.5 \ \text{cm}^3
\end{array}
$$

The section with the largest plastic modulus under 600 mm deep is a 533 × 210 × 122 UB. The plastic modulus of this section is 3 196 cm³ and clearly this is too small. It should also be noted that the flange thickness is greater than 16 mm, therefore, the maximum design strength is 265 N/mm².

The section must be strengthened with plates to provide the additional modulus and possibly stiffness.

The following will be required of the section:

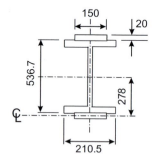

(a) A shear force of 442 kN requires a web area of

$$
\frac{442 \times 10^3}{0.6 \times 265} = 2\,780 \ \text{mm}^2.
$$

(b) A plastic modulus of 3 958.5 cm³, assuming a material thickness between 16 mm and 63 mm.

(c) A stiffness to ensure that there are no deflection problems. The maximum deflection being taken in this example is span/360.

$$Maximum\ deflection = \frac{9\,500}{360} = 26.4 \text{ mm}$$

The second moment of area ($I$) of the required beam section capable of satisfying the deflection requirement, based on unfactored imposed load, must be at least equal to:

$$I = \frac{5}{384} \frac{(3 \times 15 \times 9.5 \times 1\,000) \times (9\,500)^3}{205\,000 \times 26.4 \times 10^4} = 88\,184 \text{ cm}^4$$

Try a 533 × 210 × 101 UB with plates.

*(a) Shear check*

$$\text{Shear capacity of section} = \frac{0.6 \times 265 \times 536.7 \times 10.8}{1\,000} = 922 \text{ kN}$$

The maximum shear force is 442, which is less than 0.6 × shear capacity, i.e. 0.6 × 922 = 553 kN

∴ Section is satisfactory and there is no reduction in moment capacity.

*(b) Plastic modulus check*

The minimum plastic modulus required is 3 958.5 cm³. The UB provides 2 612 cm³.

Therefore the two equal plates must provide the remainder, 1 346.5 cm³.

Assume thickness of the plates to be 20 mm, giving a total depth of 577 mm or 57.67 cm.

Depth of UB between plates = 53.67 cm

Distance between centre to centre of plates = 53.67 + 2 = 55.67 cm

$$\text{Area required of plates} = \frac{1\,338.5}{55.67} = 24.0 \text{ cm}^2$$

Provide 150 × 20 mm plates, having an area of 30 cm².

The plastic modulus may be calculated by adding the moduli of the UB and the plates together.

$S_x$ for the compound section = 2 612 + 2 × 15 × (53.67 + 2) = 4 282 cm³

Compound section is satisfactory for moment capacity.

### (c) Deflection check

Minimum $I$ required $\qquad = 88\ 184$ cm$^4$
$I$ provided by UB $\qquad = 61\ 520$ cm$^4$
$\therefore I$ required by plates $\qquad = 26\ 664$ cm$^4$
$I$ provided by $150 \times 20$ mm plates $= 2 \times (I_g + Ah^2)$, using the parallel axis theorem, $I_g$ is normally small, see note below.

$$I = 2 \times \frac{(150 \times 20) \times 278^2}{10^4} = 46\,370 \text{ cm}^4$$

The $150 \times 20$ mm plates are satisfactory.
Total $I$ provided $= 61\ 520 + 46\ 040 = 107\ 560$ cm$^4$
Note: The second moment of area or moment of inertia of the plates ($I_g$) about their own axis is usually very small and may be neglected unless a very accurate result is required. In this case the value for the $150 \times 20$ mm plates would be:

$$\frac{2 \times 150 \times 20^3}{12 \times 10\,000} = 20 \text{ cm}^4$$

### 6.9.2 Curtailment of flange plates

The bending moment diagram for a simply supported beam carrying a UDL varies parabolically throughout the length of the beam (Fig. 6.6(a)). It would then be ideal if $I$ were to vary, making the flanges thicker towards the centre of the beam. But for practical reasons this is not possible and the total resistance moment of a beam of uniform section is shown in Fig. 6.6(b). In plated beams, the flange plates can be curtailed near the supports of the beam resulting in some steel saving. The effect of curtailment is shown in Fig. 6.6(c).

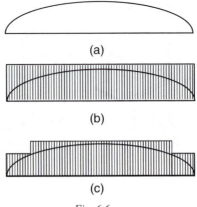

(a)

(b)

(c)

*Fig. 6.6.*

The appropriate points, usually termed theoretical cut-off points, may be found in two ways:

(a) by the algebraic method

(b) by a geometrical construction

*Example 6.9.2. Find the theoretical cut-off points for the plates computed in example 6.9.1.*

## SOLUTION

### (a) Algebraic method

The bending moment carried by the $533 \times 210 \times 101$ UB is

$$\frac{2\,612 \times 265}{10^3} = 692 \text{ kNm}$$

The distance from the support to the point where the bending moment ordinate has this value must now be found.

At any point, distance $x$ from the support:

$$M_x = Rx - \frac{wx^2}{2} \qquad \text{(see Fig. 6.7(a))}$$

Where:

$M_x = 692$ kNm, for the resistance of the beam

$R = 442.0$ kN

$w = 93$ kN/m.

Substituting:

$$692 = 442\,x - \frac{93}{2}\,x^2$$

Dividing both sides by 93/2:

$$14.88 = 9.50x - x^2$$

Rearranging:

$$x^2 - 9.50x + 14.88 = 0$$

Solving the equation

$$x = \frac{9.5 \pm \sqrt{9.5^2 - \left(4 \times 14.88\right)}}{2} = \frac{9.5 \pm 5.5}{2} = 7.5 \text{ m} \quad \text{or} \quad 2.0 \text{ m}$$

So, the theoretical cut-off points are 2.0 m from either end.

### (b) Geometrical construction

The moment capacity of the UB and each of the plates can be superimposed on the bending moment diagram of the compound beam.

The theoretical cut-off points may be taken as the points where the moment capacity of the UB intersects the curve of the bending moment diagram (see Fig. 6.7(b)).

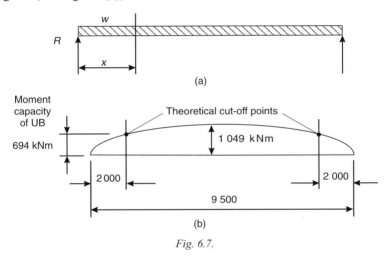

*Fig. 6.7.*

The plates must extend beyond the point where they are no longer needed in theory to enable the stresses to be transferred into them.

No precise rules are given in BS 5950. However, it would seem prudent to extend the plates far enough to generate the stresses that would be in the plate when considered as part of the compound section.

In this example, the moment at the theoretical cut-off point is 694 kNm, giving a stress in the top of the plates of $\dfrac{694 \times 287 \times 10^6}{107\,560 \times 10^4} = 185 \text{ N/mm}^2$.

At the top of the flange the stress is:

$$\frac{694 \times 267 \times 10^6}{107\,560 \times 10^4} = 172 \text{ N/mm}^2$$

Average stress in the plate $= \dfrac{185 + 172}{2} = 178.5 \text{ N/mm}^2$

Force in the plate $= 178.5 \times 15 \times \dfrac{20}{10^3} = 535.5 \text{ kN}$

Assume an 8 mm fillet weld with a capacity of 1.2 kN/mm (see Fig. 9.23).

Length of weld to develop the force in the plate =

$$\left[\frac{535.5}{(1.2 \times 2)}\right] + (2 \times 8) = 239.0 \text{ mm}$$

The distance from the support to the practical cut-off point is therefore 2.00 – 0.239, say 1.75 m.

## 6.10. Plate girders

In steel beam design, cases occur when the loads or spans are too large for universal sections or the allowable depth restricts the use of universal sections. In these cases, beams are fabricated by joining plates together. Historically, before welding became the normal method of joining plates, they were connected using rolled angles riveted to the plates as shown in Fig. 6.8(a). Modern methods involve welding the web to the flanges with fillet or butt welds (Fig. 6.8(b)).

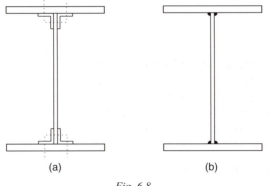

(a)                    (b)

*Fig. 6.8.*

BS 5950 gives basic design methods as follows:

A  If the depth of the web divided by the thickness is less than $62\varepsilon$ then the section may be designed in accordance with the rules for rolled sections, providing any bending stress changes are used.

B  If the shear is less than 0.6 of the shear resistance of the web then the moment capacity may be determined as though it were a simple beam.

C  If the shear is higher than this then the section may be designed by taking all the shear on the web and all the bending on the flanges, with each flange taking a uniform stress not exceeding $p_y$. This method may also be conservatively used for the first two conditions.

D  A more complex method given in BS 5950: Annex H may be used, subject to certain restrictions.

When the engineer is not constrained by other factors, the span to depth ratio, for economical design, will normally vary from 10:1 to 20:1, but if very heavy loads are to be carried on short spans this may fall to 8:1. (When designing bridge girders, where the moments are high compared to the shear, a guide to the section proportions is to make the flanges equal in area to the web. The resulting section will probably be deeper than would be acceptable in building construction.) The attention of the reader is drawn to some of the recent developments in the portal frame market. In this area a number of firms are producing frames from thin plate. These are being welded up with small single-sided welds; the frames are tapered following the shape of the bending moment diagram. In designing such frames, the engineer may consider the sections as slender cross-section plate girders.

### Web design

In the rules for web design, two routes are adopted depending on the $d/t$ (depth/thickness) ratio of the web. If this is less than $62\varepsilon$ (where $\varepsilon = \sqrt{275/p_y}$ ) then the web strength is given as $0.6\, p_y\, dt$.

If the depth to thickness ratio is greater than this then the web must be designed using the rules in §4.4.5.

The behaviour of the web during loading to failure may be considered in three stages:

A  Elastic range. During this stage the web panel remains elastic and flat. The stresses in the section are entirely elastic and may be calculated using the classic methods given in standard textbooks on the subject. The only requirement for the stiffeners is that they keep the web flat.

B  Post-buckling range. When the load reaches the elastic limit, the compressive shear stresses cause the web plate to buckle leaving the tension stresses to carry the load. At the same time, the stiffeners begin to act as struts in addition to their function of keeping the web plate flat. The tension field is starting to take effect, as shown in Fig. 6.9.

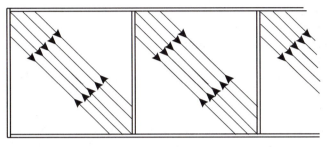

*Fig. 6.9.*

During this stage, it is assumed in the code rules that the forces developed in forming the tension field are resisted by the stiffeners and end posts.

C  Failure of the end posts and flanges. As the ultimate load is reached, the end posts and flanges, at the ends of the member where the shear is the highest, start to fail by forming plastic hinges (see Fig. 6.10). This final stage of failure will frequently take place at a load very much higher than the elastic critical value. There will be gross distortions of the web and either or both the end posts and flanges.

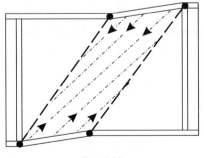

*Fig. 6.10.*

Following this simple look at the basic concept of web behaviour, a study can now be made of the methods employed in the code.

*(1) Elastic critical stress*

The shear buckling resistance, $V_b$, of a web may be taken, §4.4.5.2, as the simple shear buckling resistance, $V_b$, given by:

$$V_b = V_w = dtq_w$$

where:
$d$ is the depth of the web
$t$ is the web thickness
$q_w$ is the shear buckling strength.

The value of $q_w$ is obtained from Table 21 of the code. This table takes into account the depth of the web and the spacing of the stiffeners at the point on the span being considered.

Providing this method is employed, there is no requirement for the use of stiffeners to resist tension field action.

*(2) Method not using the effect of the flanges*

If the flanges are fully stressed in bending, then the shear resistance is still taken as $V_b$.

*(3) Flange dependent shear strength*

If the flange plates are not fully stressed in bending, the case frequently met at the support of a beam, then the contribution of the flange strength towards the resistance to shear may be considered, see §4.4.5.3.

*Example 6.10.1. A simply-supported welded plate girder for heavy power installation, consisting of two 500 × 25 mm flange plates and a 1 200 × 16 mm web plate, is required to carry a factored UDL of 3 500 kN over a span of 7 500 mm. It may be assumed that the compression flange is fully restrained. All plates are of grade S 275 steel.*

*Find (1) average flange stress and compare it with the design stress; (2) average shear stress; (3) see if stiffeners are required.*

SOLUTION

The compression flange is assumed to have adequate lateral restraint as required by §4.2.2. A cross-section of the girder is shown in Fig. 6.11.

1. If the flanges only are assumed to carry the bending moment, a conservative assumption, then the solution is as follows:

   $M = 3\ 500 \times 7.5/8 = 3\ 281.0$ kNm

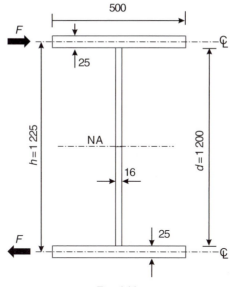

*Fig. 6.11.*

$$\text{Flange force} = M/h \frac{3\,281 \times 10^3}{1.225} = 2\,678.0\,\text{kN}$$

In this case, a local buckling check must be made. As the strength of the flange has been calculated using elastic methods the $b/t$ for a semi-compact section is appropriate.

For a welded section $b/t$ is $13\varepsilon$ (Table 11) where $\varepsilon = \sqrt{275/p_y}$

As the design strength $p_y$ is 265 N/mm² (plate thickness greater than 16 mm), $\varepsilon$ becomes 1.02, thus giving a limiting value for $b/t$ of 13.3.

$$\text{The actual } b/t = \frac{(500 - 16)}{(2 \times 25)} = 9.7$$

This is, therefore, satisfactory and no reduction is required for local buckling.

2.  Shear stress

$$\text{The maximum reaction} = \frac{3\,500}{2} = 1\,750\,\text{kN}$$

(This is also the maximum shear force.)

$$\text{Average shear stress} = \frac{1\,750 \times 10^3}{(1\,200 \times 16)} = 91\,\text{N/mm}^2$$

3. Check on stiffener requirements

$$d/t \text{ of the web} = \frac{1\,200}{16} = 75$$

$q_w$ (shear strength) $=148$ N/mm$^2$ for this $d/t$ ratio with no stiffeners ($a/d =$ ) (Table 21)

In the case of the chosen section, the flanges are adequate and no stiffeners are required for the web.

If, in this example, a 12 mm thick web plate was used in place of 16 mm then the ratio of $d/t = 1\,200/12 = 100$.

The average shear stress would then be:

$$1750 \times \frac{10^3}{\left(1\,200 \times 12\right)} = 121\,\text{N/mm}^2$$

Stiffeners are now required to give an $a/d$ ratio $= 2.5$ (Table 21) at a $q_w$ of 123 N/mm$^2$.

$$\text{Stiffener spacing} = 2.5 \times \frac{1\,200}{1\,000} = 3.0\,\text{m}$$

Both these solutions are safe. The choice facing the engineer is between economy of material using a thin plate with stiffeners at a high labour cost or a thick plate and very little labour.

If an 8 mm plate is used, the solution becomes unsafe because the average shear stress is now $1\,750 \times 10^3 / \left(1\,200 \times 8\right) = 182$ N/mm$^2$. This is higher than the allowable shear strength of 165 N/mm$^2$, the maximum allowable for any $d/t$ or $a/d$ ratio in grade S 275 steel, even with the use of stiffeners.

# 7. Compression and tension members

## 7.1. Definitions and types of compression members

A member subjected to longitudinal compressive load is usually called a strut. A vertical strut is often called a column, although this term is frequently used for a concrete vertical strut. For a vertical steel strut the term stanchion is sometimes used.

Struts are divided into three groups:

- Short struts
- Medium struts
- Long or slender struts

Most practical struts are of medium length and fall into the second group.

The terms *long* and *short* refer to the relationship between the length of the member and its cross-sectional dimensions. A 150 mm concrete cube is a short strut while a television aerial 50 mm long is a long strut.

Long struts will fail by buckling or lateral bending, while short struts tend to fail by direct crushing of the material.

When the load is applied on the axis of the centre of gravity of the cross-section, the strut is said to be *axially loaded*, and the stress produced in the material is said to be a direct compressive stress. This stress is uniform over the cross-section of the strut. The term *concentric loading* is sometimes used instead of axial loading. When the load is not axial then the strut is said to be *eccentrically loaded* (meaning off-centre) and bending stress is induced in the strut in addition to direct compressive stress.

## 7.2. Parameters determining the axial load

The maximum axial load which a strut can carry depends on the material of which the strut is made and on the 'slenderness' of the strut; the magnitude of the latter is determined by the length or height of the strut and the manner in which its ends are supported, and the size and the shape of its cross-section.

Some simple experiments can be performed to illustrate these effects.

*First experiment.* Take a piece of timber 500 mm long of, say, 50 mm × 4 mm cross-section; apply a load with the hand at the top while holding it vertically, with the other end resting on the floor. Some lateral bending occurs at right angles to the shorter dimension of the cross-sectional area.

Now take a 250 mm long piece of the same cross-section and apply the same load. It will be seen that the lateral bending is not as large as in the first case.

*Second experiment.* Take a piece of timber 500 mm long of 25 mm × 8 mm cross-section. Applying the same force, it can be seen that the more slender section, that of 50 mm × 4 mm, is the weaker of the two.

*Third experiment.* Take a plastic scale 350 mm long and, holding it between the index fingers, apply some axial load. The scale will bend easily. In order to obtain the same bending, when the scale is gripped tightly would require a greater load.

## 7.3. Radius of gyration and slenderness ratio

It has previously been stated that the slenderness of a strut depends on (i) the second moment of area or moment of inertia ($I$) and (ii) the sectional area ($A$). It has been shown that the association of these two quantities is in the form of the square root of their ratio; this property is called radius of gyration and is usually denoted by $r$.

$$r = \sqrt{\frac{I}{A}}$$

From the simple experiments described earlier, it was shown that lateral bending would be about the weaker axis of the section. Therefore, in the calculation of the stiffness, the radius of gyration taken must be calculated using the lesser moment of inertia. In the case of a steel I-beam the weaker axis is Y–Y so the lesser moment of inertia is $I_y$.

$$\text{Radius of gyration } r_y = \sqrt{\frac{I_y}{A}}$$

The simple experiments also showed that the conditions of end fixity contribute to the determination of the axial load. These conditions come into the calculation under the term effective length ($L_E$); this is the unsupported or actual length ($L$) multiplied by a factor, which depends upon the end conditions.

The ratio between effective length and the radius of gyration is known as the slenderness ratio, denoted by $\lambda$ in BS 5950.

$$\text{Slenderness ratio } \lambda = \frac{L_E}{r}$$

The effective length to be used in calculating the slenderness ratio of a compression member is governed by §4.7.2 and §4.7.3 and Annexes B, D and E in BS 5950. The rules given in Annex E are intended for use when designing fully-rigid structures and will not be considered at this stage. The other clauses give rules for struts in simple multi-storey frames. Annex D gives illustrations of effective lengths of columns in single storey structures. Seven common cases are considered, as shown in Table 22 from BS 5950, reproduced below. (It should be noted that the connections will not necessarily provide the full rotational restraint required to give the effective length derived from the Euler calculations, therefore Table 22 gives longer effective lengths than would be obtained from theory.)

*BS 5950 Table 22: Nominal effective length, $L_E$, for compression members* *

**(a) Non-sway mode**

| Restraint (in the plane under consideration) by other parts of the structure | | $L_E$ |
|---|---|---|
| Effectively held in position at both ends | Effectively restrained in direction at both ends | 0.7L |
| | Partially restrained in direction at both ends | 0.85L |
| | Restrained in direction at one end | 0.85L |
| | Not restrained in direction at either end | 1.0L |

**(b) Sway mode**

| One end | Other end | | $L_E$ |
|---|---|---|---|
| Effectively held in position and restrained in direction | Not held in position | Effectively restrained in direction | 1.2L |
| | | Partially restrained in direction | 1.5L |
| | | Not restrained in direction | 2.0L |

* Excluding angle, channel or T-section struts designed in accordance with §4.7.10

## 7.4. Euler theory for long struts

A Swiss mathematician named Leonhard Euler (1707–83) used mathematical considerations to derive a formula for the strength of a long pin-ended strut. He based his formula on the following assumptions:

- The struts are very long in proportion to their cross-sectional dimensions.
- The struts are initially perfectly straight and homogeneous in quality.
- The compressive loads are perfectly axially applied.
- The struts are uniform throughout and the limit of proportionality of the material is not exceeded so that the assumptions in the theory of simple bending can be applied.

Euler found that the buckling or critical load, $P$, for long struts with both ends pinned is given by:

$$P = \frac{\pi^2 EI}{L_E^2} \tag{7.I}$$

Note: The derivation of the formula may be found in any book on the theory of structures.

For built-in or fixed ended struts:

$$P = \frac{4\pi^2 EI}{L_E^2} \tag{7.II}$$

Note: The struts were assumed to have equal moments of inertia about the two principal axes.

The Euler formula can be put into a more convenient form. Taking equation (7.I), multiply above and below by $A$, the cross-sectional area.

$$P = \frac{\pi^2 EI}{L_E^2} \times \frac{A}{A} = \frac{\pi^2 EA}{L_E^2} \times \frac{I}{A} \tag{7.III}$$

$$\text{But } \frac{I}{A} = r^2 \tag{7.IV}$$

$$\therefore P = \frac{\pi^2 EA}{L_E^2} \times r^2 \tag{7.V}$$

Rearranging equation (7.V)

$$\frac{P}{A} = \frac{\pi^2 E}{\left(\dfrac{L_E}{r}\right)^2} = \frac{\pi^2 E}{\lambda^2} \tag{7.VI}$$

Note: In the case where there are two different values of the slenderness ratio about the two principal axes, the maximum value controls the design.

## 7.5. Practical design of struts

For the design of long struts, equation (7.VI) applies with the insertion of a factor of safety ($\gamma_f$), i.e.

$$\frac{P}{A} = \frac{E}{\gamma_f} \times \frac{\pi^2}{\left(\dfrac{L_E}{r}\right)^2} = \frac{E}{\gamma_f} \times \frac{\pi^2}{\lambda^2} \qquad (7.\text{VII})$$

The long strut fails by buckling and the stress causing failure depends on the slenderness ratio and the modulus of elasticity of the material.

For the design of short struts, equation (7.VIII) applies, inserting again the factor of safety ($\gamma_f$).

$$f = \frac{P}{A} \times \frac{1}{\gamma_f} \qquad (7.\text{VIII})$$

The short strut fails by the overstressing of the material in compression and therefore the stress causing failure does not depend on the slenderness ratio or the modulus of elasticity of the material.

If stress is plotted against slenderness ratio, as in Fig. 7.1, equation (7.VIII) is a straight line, since stress is independent of the slenderness ratio, and equation (7.VII) is a hyperbola, since the stress is inversely proportional to the square of the slenderness ratio.

The experimental stress values of struts, for a slenderness ratio less than 20, are close enough to the values obtained by the short strut formula in order to be considered the same.

However, for medium struts, where the slenderness ratio varies between 20 and 100, neither the stress values obtained by the short strut formula nor those obtained by the Euler formula are close to the experimental stress values. Therefore other formulae have to be derived in order to obtain satisfactory agreement showing that the conditions of failure of medium struts cannot be simply determined.

Euler's formula is applicable only to long struts with large slenderness ratios; because the majority of practical struts are of medium length Euler's formula is not used directly for structural design. Euler's work, however, was of great importance to other research workers who have attempted to evolve a rational basis for strut design. Indeterminate factors, such as the amount of initial curvature, accidental eccentricity of loading, and the extent of end fixity, make an exact solution impossible, and a number of empirical formulae have been proposed.

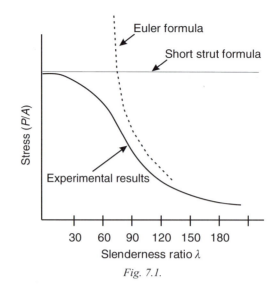

*Fig. 7.1.*

Since the late 1940s, steelwork has been designed in Britain and Ireland to formulae laid down in codes of practice or specifications. These are based on Professor Perry's formula, which takes into account the probable initial curvature.

This formula has now been revised and re-presented in BS 5950, and the effects of initial imperfections, residual stresses and section shapes have been included in more detail. The changes to the basic formula are concerned with the derivation of the Perry factor, $\eta$. The values now used give results which closely correspond with the European codes and international values derived from test results. The basic Perry formula is quoted as:

$$p_c = \frac{p_E \, p_y}{\varphi + \left(\varphi^2 - p_E \, p_y\right)^{0.5}}$$

where:

$$\varphi = \frac{p_y + (\eta + 1) p_E}{2}$$

$p_E$ is the Euler strength, $\left(\dfrac{\pi^2 E}{\lambda^2}\right)$

$p_y$ is the design strength

$\eta$ is the Perry factor for flexural buckling under load, which should be obtained from:

$$\eta = 0.001a \, (\lambda - \lambda_0) \geq 0$$

where:

*a* is the Robertson constant, which has the following values:

2.0 for BS 5950 Table 24(a)
3.5 for BS 5950 Table 24(b)
5.5 for BS 5950 Table 24(c)
8.0 for BS 5950 Table 24(d)

$\lambda$ is the slenderness

$\lambda_0$ is the limiting slenderness, which should be taken as $0.2\left(\dfrac{\pi^2 E}{p_y}\right)^{0.5}$.

Looking at the expression for $\eta$, the value of *a* selects the appropriate BS 5950 Table (24(a) or 24(b) or 24(c) or 24(d)). The selection of the table is based on the type of section, as given in BS 5950 Table 23 and Fig. 14. It will be found that those sections that have the lowest residual stresses will be designed on the highest strut curves. The value in the bracket makes adjustments for the length of the member and the horizontal 'plateau' at low slenderness ratios. If $\lambda$ is less than $\lambda_0$ then the calculated value of the average axial stress would exceed the design strength ($p_y$). This is prevented by limiting the value to $p_y$, giving the plateau found in tests. The limiting slenderness, $\lambda_0$, has been set at 0.2 of the Euler strut value for the design strength, making the plateau length less than 20. Fig. 7.2 illustrates typical curves.

For welded I-, H- or box sections, §4.7.5 states that $p_c$ should be obtained from BS 5950 Table 24 using a value of $p_y$, 20 N/mm² below that obtained from §3.1.1. This takes account of the severe residual stresses and possible distortion due to welding.

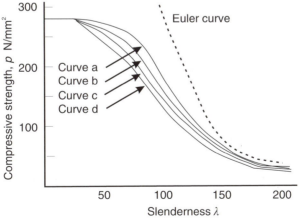

*Fig. 7.2.*

Design procedure for axially loaded struts:

- Determine ultimate axial load.
- Determine effective length from BS 5950 Table 22 or Annex D.
- Select a trial section.
- Check for local buckling.
- Calculate $\lambda$.
- Using BS 5950 Table 23 and Table 14, determine suitable strut curve.
- Using BS 5950 Table 24(a), (b), (c) or (d), determine compressive strength, $p_c$.
- Calculate axial load capacity or compression resistance, $P_c$.
- Check against applied load.

*Example 7.5.1. An uncased 152 × 152 × 37 UC, 3 m long, is fixed at both ends. Find the load capacity if the steel is grade S 275, which has a design strength of 275 N/mm².*

## SOLUTION

Effective length $(L_E) = 0.7 \times$ actual length $(L)$.

$L_E = 0.7 \times 3 = 2.1$ m

Properties of section:

Area $= 47.1$ cm²

$I_y = 706$ cm⁴ and $I_x = 2\,210$ cm⁴

$r_y$ (minimum radius of gyration) $= 3.87$ cm

Local buckling check:

This section is subjected to uniform loading in compression so the requirement is that the section is at least semi-compact, i.e. not slender. The section must, therefore, be checked to ensure that it complies with the requirements of BS 5950 Table 11 for a semi-compact section. In this instance the limits are:

For the flange, $b/t$ must be less than $15\varepsilon$.
For the web the $d/t$ ratio must be less then $40\varepsilon$.
The value of $\varepsilon$ is taken from the design strength
From Table 11, $\varepsilon = \sqrt{275/p_y}$

The value of $p_y$ is 275 N/mm².

$\therefore \varepsilon = 1.0$

That gives limits of 15 and 40 for the two ratios.

The outstand ratio of the flange of this section is:

$$\frac{154.4}{2 \times 11.5} = 6.7$$

The $d/t$ of the web is:

$$\frac{123.6}{8.0} = 15.45$$

This section, therefore, complies with the requirements for a semi-compact section and may be used as a simple strut without any local buckling restrictions.

Slenderness ratio $= (2.1 \times 10^2)/3.87 = 54.3$

From BS 5950 Table 23, this section should be checked using BS 5950 Table 24(c) for the value of $p_c$. This gives an average axial stress $= 213$ N/mm$^2$.

Axial load capacity or compressive resistance, $P_c$

$$= 47.1 \times \frac{213}{10} = 1\,003 \text{ kN}.$$

*Example 7.5.2. An uncased 457 × 191 × 74 UB is acting as a pin-ended column, 4 m long. What is the load capacity, allowing for any local buckling, and assuming it is made from grade S 275 steel with a yield stress of 275 N/mm²?*

SOLUTION

Effective length $(L_E) = 1 \times$ actual length $(L)$

$$L_E = 4 \text{ m}$$

Properties of section:

$A = 94.6$ cm$^2$
$I_y = 1\,671$ cm$^4$
$r_y = 4.20$ cm

Local buckling:

From BS 5950 Table 11, $\varepsilon = \sqrt{275/275} = 1$

Limiting outstand ratios of flanges and web for a semi-compact section are $15\varepsilon$ and $40\varepsilon$ respectively.

Actual values for selected section:

$$\text{Flange} = \frac{190.4}{2 \times 14.5} = 6.57$$

$$\text{Web} = \frac{407.6}{9.0} = 45.3$$

The flanges comply with these limitations but the web is clearly slender. Fig. 8 in BS 5950 shows the effective area of the web to be $20t\varepsilon$ from the root radii at each side of the web $= 20 \times 9.0 = 180$ mm.

The effective area of the web will, therefore, be

$$\frac{2 \times 180 \times 9.0}{10^3} = 32.4 \text{ cm}^2$$

The total area of the web between root radii is $\dfrac{407.8 \times 9.0}{10^2} = 36.7 \text{cm}^2$

The area of the section is, therefore, reduced by $36.7 - 32.4 = 4.3 \text{ cm}^2$

The slenderness ratio $\left(\dfrac{L_E}{r_y}\right) = \dfrac{4 \times 10^2}{4.20} = 95.2$

Using BS 5950 Table 23, the strength is taken from BS 5950 Table 24(b). From this table, $p_c = 150$ N/mm$^2$

Axial load capacity or compression resistance $=$
$$(94.6 - 4.3) \times \frac{150}{10} = 1355 \text{ kN}$$

Note: Stanchions are sometimes braced differently about the major and minor axes as shown by stanchion AB in Fig. 7.3.

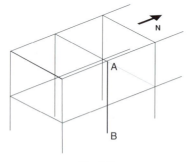

*Fig. 7.3.*

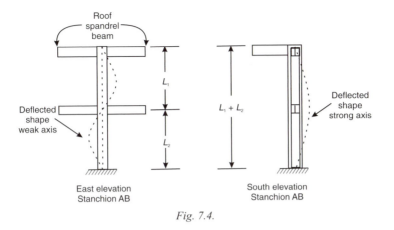

*Fig. 7.4.*

If all connections to the stanchion are assumed to be pinned, the deflected shapes for buckling about the two axes will be as shown in Fig. 7.4.

Observe that the stanchion is braced so that the unbraced length for the weak axis buckling is less than the unbraced length for buckling about the strong axis. In this situation, either axis may control failure depending on which has the smallest slenderness ratio. It should be noted that the curve for failure about the weak axis is lower than that for strong axis failure; this may affect the way in which failure takes place. (Naturally, if there is no reasonable certainty that the bracing will not be removed, the stanchion should be designed with the bracing neglected.)

## 7.6. Design of angle struts

The internal struts of roof trusses and bracing members frequently consist of single angle sections. These are attached by one leg to gusset plates or the chord members. Such attachment will be by bolting or welding one leg of the angle, thus the centre of gravity of the connection will not coincide with the centroid of the section. To speed the design process, §4.7.10, allows the engineer to design the strut as a simple compression member subjected to certain limitations. These are:

The length $L$ should be taken as the distance between the intersection of centroidal axes or the intersections of the setting out lines of the bolts, and $r$ is the radius of gyration about the relevant axis. Axes are defined in Fig. 7.5, on the following pages.

*BS 5950 Table 25. Discontinuous angle, channel and T section struts.*

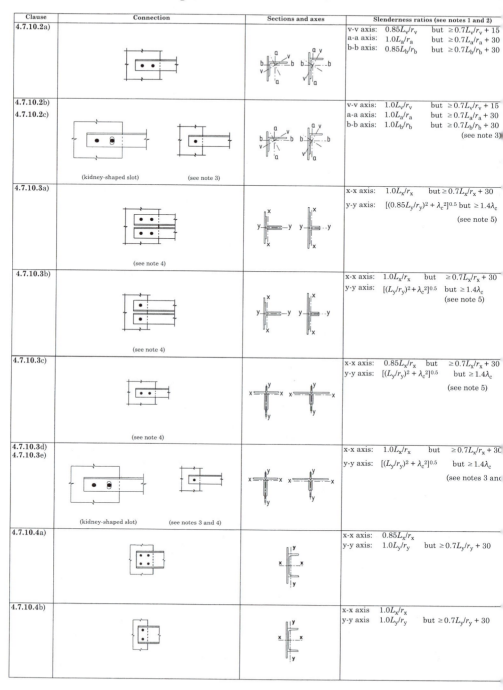

| Clause | Connection | Sections and axes | Slenderness ratios (see notes 1 and 2) |
|---|---|---|---|
| **4.7.10.2a)** | | | v-v axis: $0.85L_v/r_v$ but $\geq 0.7L_v/r_v + 15$ <br> a-a axis: $1.0L_a/r_a$ but $\geq 0.7L_a/r_a + 30$ <br> b-b axis: $0.85L_b/r_b$ but $\geq 0.7L_b/r_b + 30$ |
| **4.7.10.2b)** <br> **4.7.10.2c)** | (kidney-shaped slot)　　(see note 3) | | v-v axis: $1.0L_v/r_v$ but $\geq 0.7L_v/r_v + 15$ <br> a-a axis: $1.0L_a/r_a$ but $\geq 0.7L_a/r_a + 30$ <br> b-b axis: $1.0L_b/r_b$ but $\geq 0.7L_b/r_b + 30$ <br> (see note 3) |
| **4.7.10.3a)** | (see note 4) | | x-x axis: $1.0L_x/r_x$ but $\geq 0.7L_x/r_x + 30$ <br> y-y axis: $[(0.85L_y/r_y)^2 + \lambda_c^2]^{0.5}$ but $\geq 1.4\lambda_c$ <br> (see note 5) |
| **4.7.10.3b)** | (see note 4) | | x-x axis: $1.0L_x/r_x$ but $\geq 0.7L_x/r_x + 30$ <br> y-y axis: $[(L_y/r_y)^2 + \lambda_c^2]^{0.5}$ but $\geq 1.4\lambda_c$ <br> (see note 5) |
| **4.7.10.3c)** | (see note 4) | | x-x axis: $0.85L_x/r_x$ but $\geq 0.7L_x/r_x + 30$ <br> y-y axis: $[(L_y/r_y)^2 + \lambda_c^2]^{0.5}$ but $\geq 1.4\lambda_c$ <br> (see note 5) |
| **4.7.10.3d)** <br> **4.7.10.3e)** | (kidney-shaped slot)　　(see notes 3 and 4) | | x-x axis: $1.0L_x/r_x$ but $\geq 0.7L_x/r_x + 30$ <br> y-y axis: $[(L_y/r_y)^2 + \lambda_c^2]^{0.5}$ but $\geq 1.4\lambda_c$ <br> (see notes 3 and ...) |
| **4.7.10.4a)** | | | x-x axis: $0.85L_x/r_x$ <br> y-y axis: $1.0L_y/r_y$ but $\geq 0.7L_y/r_y + 30$ |
| **4.7.10.4b)** | | | x-x axis $1.0L_x/r_x$ <br> y-y axis $1.0L_y/r_y$ but $\geq 0.7L_y/r_y + 30$ |

*Fig. 7.5(a)*

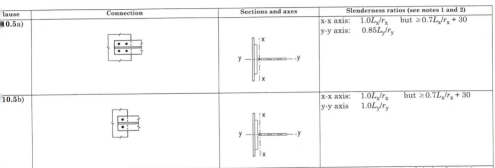

| lause | Connection | Sections and axes | Slenderness ratios (see notes 1 and 2) |
|---|---|---|---|
| 10.5a) | | | x-x axis: $1.0L_x/r_x$ but $\geq 0.7L_x/r_x + 30$<br>y-y axis: $0.85L_y/r_y$ |
| 10.5b) | | | x-x axis: $1.0L_x/r_x$ but $\geq 0.7L_x/r_x + 30$<br>y-y axis $1.0L_y/r_y$ |

'E 1   The length $L$ is taken between the intersections of the centroidal axes or the intersections of the setting out lines of the bolts, irrespective of whether the strut is ected to a gusset or directly to another member.

'E 2   Intermediate restraints reduce the value of $L$ for buckling about the relevant axes. For single angle members, $L_v$ is taken between lateral restraints, perpendicular to ir a-a or b-b.

'E 3   For single or double angles connected by one bolt, the compression resistance is also reduced to 80 % of that for an axially loaded member, see **4.7.10.2b)** or **4.7.10.3d)**.

'E 4   Double angles are either battened (see **4.7.12**) or interconnected back-to-back (see **4.7.13**). Battens or interconnecting bolts are also needed at the ends of members.

'E 5   $\lambda_c = L_v/r_v$ with $L_v$ measured between interconnecting bolts for back-to-back struts, or between end welds or end bolts of adjacent battens for battened angle struts.

*Fig. 7.5(a) (cont.)*

BS 5950 Table 11.  *Limiting width-to-thickness ratios for sections other than CHS and RHS.*

| Compression element | | Ratio[a] | Limiting value[b] | | |
|---|---|---|---|---|---|
| | | | Class 1<br>plastic | Class 2<br>compact | Class 3<br>semi-compact |
| Outstand element of<br>compression flange | Rolled section | $b/T$ | $9\varepsilon$ | $10\varepsilon$ | $15\varepsilon$ |
| | Welded section | $b/T$ | $8\varepsilon$ | $9\varepsilon$ | $13\varepsilon$ |
| Internal element of<br>compression flange | Compression due<br>to bending | $b/T$ | $28\varepsilon$ | $32\varepsilon$ | $40\varepsilon$ |
| | Axial compression | $b/T$ | Not applicable | | |
| Web of an I-,<br>H- or box<br>section[c] | Neutral axis at mid-depth | $d/t$ | $80\varepsilon$ | $100\varepsilon$ | $120\varepsilon$ |
| | Generally[d] If $r_1$ is negative: | $d/t$ | | $\dfrac{100\varepsilon}{1+r_1}$ | |
| | If $r_1$ is positive: | $d/t$ | $\dfrac{80\varepsilon}{1+r_1}$<br><br>but $\geq 40\varepsilon$ | $\dfrac{100\varepsilon}{1+1.5r_1}$<br><br>but $\geq 40\varepsilon$ | $\dfrac{120\varepsilon}{1+2r_2}$<br><br>but $\geq 40\varepsilon$ |
| | Axial compression[d] | $d/t$ | Not applicable | | |
| Web of a channel | | $d/t$ | $40\varepsilon$ | $40\varepsilon$ | $40\varepsilon$ |
| Angle, compression due to bending<br>(Both criteria should be satisfied) | | $b/t$<br>$d/t$ | $9\varepsilon$<br>$9\varepsilon$ | $10\varepsilon$<br>$10\varepsilon$ | $15\varepsilon$<br>$15\varepsilon$ |
| Single angle, or double angles with the<br>components separated, axial compression<br>(All three criteria should be satisfied) | | $b/t$<br>$d/t$<br>$(b+d)/t$ | Not applicable | | $15\varepsilon$<br>$15\varepsilon$<br>$24\varepsilon$ |
| Outstand leg of an angle in contact<br>back-to-back in a double angle member | | $b/t$ | $9\varepsilon$ | $10\varepsilon$ | $15\varepsilon$ |
| Outstand leg of an angle with its back in<br>continuous contact with another component | | | | | |
| Stem of a T-section, rolled or cut from a rolled<br>I- or H-section | | $D/t$ | $8\varepsilon$ | $9\varepsilon$ | $18\varepsilon$ |

a   Dimensions $b$, $D$, $d$, $T$ and $t$ are defined in Figure 5. For a box section $b$ and $T$ are flange dimensions and $d$ and $t$ are web dimensions, where the distinction between webs and flanges depends upon whether the box section is bent about its major axis or its minor axis, see **3.5.1**.

b   The parameter $\varepsilon = (275/p_y)^{0.5}$.

c   For the web of a hybrid section $\varepsilon$ should be based on the design strength $p_{yf}$ of the flanges.

d   The stress ratios $r_1$ and $r_2$ are defined in **3.5.5**.

*Fig. 7.5(b)*

*Example 7.6.1. Design, in grade S 275 steel, a discontinuous angle strut with single bolted connections to carry a factored load of 62 kN.*
*Effective length = actual length = 2 m.*

## SOLUTION

Try $70 \times 70 \times 10$ angle.

As the steel is grade S 275 and the thickness is less than 16 mm the design strength is taken as 275 N/mm².

$$\varepsilon = \sqrt{\frac{275}{p_y}} = \sqrt{\frac{275}{275}} = 1$$

$$\frac{b}{t} = \frac{70}{10} = 7$$

$$\frac{(b+d)}{t} = (70 + 70) \times \frac{1.0}{10} = 14 < 15\varepsilon \qquad \text{(Table 11, BS 5950)}$$

These are within the limits for a semi-compact cross-section (Table 11, BS 5950 on page 109); therefore local buckling will not be a problem, and the design may be based on the area of the whole section.

The maximum slenderness ratio will be taken as the greater of

$$1.0\, L_v/r_v \quad \text{or} \quad 0.7\, L_v/r_v \;+\; 15$$
$$\text{or} \quad 1.0\, L_a/r_a \quad \text{or} \quad 0.7\, L_a/r_a \;+\; 30$$
$$\text{or} \quad 1.0\, L_b/r_b \quad \text{or} \quad 0.7\, L_b/r_b \;+\; 30$$

where:

$v$ is the axis of the minimum radius of gyration (1.36 cm)
$a$ is the axis parallel to the connecting plate (2.09 cm)
$b$ is the axis at right angles to the connecting plate (2.09 cm).

The design slenderness ratio, $\lambda$, is the greater of:

(a) $\quad \lambda = \dfrac{1.0 \times 2 \times 100}{1.36} = 147 \text{ or } \lambda = \dfrac{0.7 \times 2 \times 100}{1.36} + 15 = 118$

(b) $\quad \lambda = \dfrac{1.0 \times 2 \times 100}{2.09} = 96 \text{ or } \lambda = \dfrac{0.7 \times 2 \times 100}{2.09} + 30 = 97$

(c)   As this is an equal angle, the radius of gyration is the same for both $a$- and $b$-axes. This means that the calculation for the value of $\lambda$ is the same as for condition $(a)$. If the angle was unequal then the radius of gyration about the $b$-axis would be used in place of that about the $a$-axis for this calculation.

Table 23 of BS 5950 refers to Table 24(c) for the compressive strength, $p_c$.

Using $\lambda = 148$ (the highest), $p_c = 70$ N/mm² from BS 5950 Table 24(c).

The area of the section is 13.10 cm².

Capacity or compressive resistance (stress × area)
$= 70 \times 13.10/10 = 92$ kN.

Because there is only one bolt at each end, this is reduced to 0.8 of the capacity to give $0.8 \times 92 = 73$ kN.

This is greater than the load of 62 kN and is therefore satisfactory.

*Example 7.6.2. Design the same discontinuous angle strut assuming that two bolts are provided at each end for the same load of 62 kN.*

### SOLUTION

Try $60 \times 60 \times 8$ angle.

$$\frac{b}{t} = \frac{60}{8} = 7.5$$

$$\frac{(b+d)}{t} = \frac{(60+60)}{8} = 15$$

These are within the limits for a semi-compact cross-section (Table 11, BS 5950), and may be designed to full stress.

Slenderness ratios (Table 25, BS 5950):

(a) $\quad \lambda = \dfrac{0.85L_v}{r_v} = \dfrac{0.85 \times 2 \times 100}{1.16} = 146$

$\quad$ or $\lambda = \dfrac{0.7L_v}{r_v} + 15 = \dfrac{0.7 \times 2 \times 100}{1.16} + 15 = 136$

(b) $\quad \lambda = \dfrac{1 \times L_a}{r_a} = \dfrac{1 \times 2 \times 100}{1.8} = 111$

$\quad$ or $\lambda = \dfrac{0.7L_a}{r_a} + 30 = \dfrac{0.7 \times 2 \times 100}{1.8} + 30 = 108$

(c) Once again we have an equal angle.

As with the previous example, Table 24(c) gives a value of $p_c$, which for $\lambda = 146$, is 71 N/mm².

Capacity or compressive resistance = stress × area

$$= 71 \times \frac{903}{10^3} = 64 \text{ kN}$$

This is greater than the applied load of 62 kN.

Note: The 60 × 60 × 8 angle weighs 7.09 kg/m and the 70 × 70 × 10 weighs 10.3 kg/m. The addition of one bolt at each end of the strut results in a 31 per cent saving of weight.

Single bolted connections are seldom used in practice.

*Example 7.6.3. Design, in grade S 275 steel, a discontinuous double angle strut consisting of 2 angles back-to-back, connected to both sides of a gusset with not less than 2 bolts in standard holes and having a length between intersections of 3 m, and carrying a load of 90 kN.*

## SOLUTION

Trial section: 75 × 50 × 6 angles, short legs outstanding.

Design strength, $p_y = 275$ N/mm² (section 16 mm thick).

The radii of gyration are:

$x$-axis = 2.37 cm

$y$-axis = 2.14 cm (both sections combined), 1.42 cm for each section alone

$v$-axis = 1.08 cm minimum axis of the individual angles

The area of the combined section = 14.30 cm².

Slenderness ratio to be taken as the greatest of (Table 25, BS 5950): Two conditions are applied:

(a) $\quad \lambda = 0.85 \dfrac{L_x}{r_x} = \dfrac{0.85 \times 3.0 \times 10^2}{2.37} = 108$

but not less than

$$\lambda = 0.7 \frac{L_x}{r_x} + 30 = \frac{0.7 \times 3.0 \times 10^2}{2.37} + 30 = 119$$

(b) $\quad \lambda = \left[ \left( \dfrac{L_y}{r_y} \right)^2 + \lambda_c^2 \right]^{0.5} \quad \text{but} \geq \lambda_c \times 1.4$

Assuming the angles are interconnected at four intermediate points along their length then the spacing of the connections will be 600 mm.

This gives $\lambda_c = 60/1.08 = 56$. It is suggested that $\lambda_c$ should have a value of about 50.

$$\frac{L_y}{r_y} = \frac{3.0 \times 10^2}{2.14} = 140.2$$

$$\lambda = \sqrt{140.2^2 + 56^2} = 151$$

From Table 24(c), the value of $p_c$ is 67 N/mm$^2$.

The compressive resistance of the section is $14.3 \times 67/10 = 95.8$ kN.

This is greater than the 90 kN required.

## 7.7. Design of hollow and compound struts

Man knew the structural advantages of the hollow section when he discovered that all conditions of stress could be resisted by a hollow section, in the form of the bones of animals or the stalk of a plant.

Hot-rolled hollow sections are made in round, square and rectangular shapes in both grade S 275 and grade S 355 steels.

Hollow sections are of special interest to designers both for their aesthetic appearance and from the point of view of structural efficiency.

The load carrying capacity of a strut depends on the slenderness ratio, as mentioned earlier. The compressive strength, $p_c$, given by Table 24 of BS 5950, reduces with increasing slenderness ratio, and it is therefore an advantage to keep the slenderness ratio of a strut as low as possible. The effective length of a strut depends on the actual length and the end conditions, and is independent of the structural shape. Therefore, the ideal section for carrying compression is one with a high radius of gyration for a given weight. The radius of gyration of hollow sections is high about both axes, because the material is concentrated away from the longitudinal axis. This means that hollow struts are very efficient struts. Also, hollow struts can be used economically in cases where the effective lengths of struts about the two principal axes are equal, despite the fact that they are more expensive than normal rolled sections.

Hollow sections may also be formed by connecting plates together (see Fig. 7.6(b)).

To illustrate the load-carrying advantage of a hollow strut, let us consider a pin-jointed strut, 3 m high, in grade S 275. At first, let the strut be a solid bar having a rectangular cross-section 150 mm × 50 mm (see Fig. 7.6(a)).

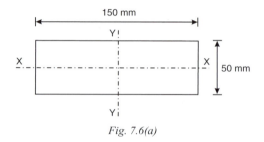

Fig. 7.6(a)

The lesser second moment of area or moment of inertia about the two principal axes is $I_x$.

$$I_x = \frac{bd^3}{12} = \frac{\left(\dfrac{150 \times 50^3}{12}\right)}{10^4} = 156.25 \text{ cm}^4$$

$$A = \frac{150 \times 50}{100} = 75.0 \text{ cm}^2$$

$$r_x = \sqrt{\frac{I_x}{A}} = \sqrt{\frac{156.25}{75.0}} = 1.443 \text{ cm}$$

$$\text{Slenderness ratio} = \frac{L_E}{r_x} = \frac{3.0 \times 100}{1.443} = 208$$

$p_c$ (assuming a strength of 275 N/mm², Table 24(a)) = 44 N/mm²

Note: For this example, the design strength will be taken as 275 N/mm² in both cases. Table 9 of BS 5950 requires a reduction of strength for a material thickness of 40 mm and over. This will not be taken into account here in order to show the full effect of changing the section.

Load capacity or compression resistance = $44 \times 75/10 = 330$ kN

Now suppose that the bar is divided into four pieces of 150 mm × 12.5 mm and these are welded to form a box section of 150 mm × 175 mm (see Fig. 7.6(b)).

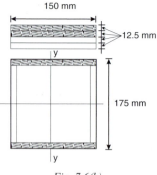

Fig. 7.6(b)

Now the lesser second moment of area or moment of inertia is $I_y$.

$$I_y = \frac{\left(\dfrac{175 \times 150^3}{12} - \dfrac{150 \times 125^3}{12}\right)}{10^4} = 2\,480 \text{ cm}^4$$

$$A = \frac{(175 \times 150 - 150 \times 125)}{10^2} = 75.0 \text{ cm}^2$$

$$r_y = \sqrt{\frac{2\,480}{75}} = 5.75 \text{ cm}$$

$$\frac{L_E}{r_y} = \frac{3 \times 100}{5.75} = 52.2$$

$$p_c = 249 \text{ N/mm}^2 \qquad\qquad \text{(BS 5950 Table 24(a))}$$

Load capacity or compression resistance $= \dfrac{249}{10} \times 75.0 = 1\,867.5$ kN

Although the area is the same in both cases, the load capacities are quite different.

*Example 7.7.1. A rectangular hollow steel strut, in grade S 275 steel, is formed by welding two 250 mm × 25 mm thick plates and two 200 mm × 25 mm thick plates to form a section of 200 mm × 300 mm overall. Calculate the axial load capacity or compression resistance if it is fixed at both ends and has a length of 3 m.*

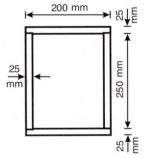

### SOLUTION

Effective length $= 0.7 \times$ actual length

$$L_E = 0.7 \times 3 = 2.1 \text{ m}$$

$$\text{Minor } I = \frac{\left(\dfrac{300 \times 200^3}{12} - \dfrac{250 \times 150^3}{12}\right)}{10^4} = 12\,969 \text{ cm}^4$$

$$A = \frac{(200 \times 300 - 150 \times 250)}{10^2} = 225 \text{ cm}^2$$

$$\text{Lesser } r = \sqrt{\frac{12\,970}{225}} = \sqrt{57.64} = 7.6 \text{ cm}$$

$$\lambda = \frac{L_E}{r} = \frac{2.1 \times 100}{7.6} = 27.6$$

For sections fabricated from plate by welding, §4.7.5 states that the value of $p_y$ should be reduced by 20 N/mm².

Using Table 24(b) and $p_y = 245$ N/mm²:

$p_c = 237$ N/mm².

$$\text{Load capacity or compression resistance} = \frac{237 \times 225.0}{10} = 5\,332.5 \text{ kN}$$

*Example 7.7.2. Calculate the safe load of a 2 m long pin-jointed hollow circular strut, in grade S 275 steel, having 75 mm outside diameter (D) and 66 mm inside diameter (d).*

### SOLUTION

$$I_y = I_x = \frac{\pi}{64}\left(D^4 - d^4\right) = \frac{\pi}{64}\left(D^2 + d^2\right)\left(D^2 - d^2\right)$$

$$A = \frac{\pi}{4}\left(D^2 - d^2\right)$$

$$r = \sqrt{\frac{\frac{\pi}{64}\left(D^2 + d^2\right)\left(D^2 - d^2\right)}{\frac{\pi}{4}\left(D^2 - d^2\right)}} = \sqrt{\frac{D^2 + d^2}{16}}$$

Substituting the values given:

$$r = \sqrt{\frac{75^2 + 66^2}{16}} = 25.0 \text{ mm}$$

$$L_E = 1.0\,L = 2 \text{ m}$$

$$\lambda = L_E/r = 2 \times 10^3/25 = 80$$

$$p_c = 203 \text{ N/mm}^2 \text{ (using Table 24(a))}$$

The area of the section:

$$A = \frac{\pi}{4}\left(D^2 - d^2\right) = \frac{\pi}{4}\left(D + d\right)\left(D - d\right)$$

$$= \frac{\pi}{4}\left(75 + 66\right)\left(75 - 66\right) = 996.7 \text{ mm}^2$$

$$\text{Capacity or compression resistance} = \frac{203}{10^3} \times 996.7 = 202 \text{ kN}$$

## 7.8. Design of cased struts

Empirical rules for the design of cased members are given in §4.14, provided the following conditions are satisfied:

a.  The steel section is either a single rolled or fabricated I- or H-section with equal flanges or two similar rolled channel sections in contact back-to-back or separated back-to-back by not less than 20 mm or more than half their depth.

b.  The overall dimensions of the steel section do not exceed 1 000 mm × 500 mm, the dimension of 1 000 mm being measured parallel to the web or webs.

c.  Primary structural connections to the member should preferably be made directly to the steel section.

d.  The steel section is unpainted and free from oil, grease, dirt and loose rust or millscale.

e.  The steel section is solidly encased in ordinary dense structural concrete of at least grade 25 strength.

f.  There is a minimum rectangle of solid casing, which may be chamfered at the corners, that provides a cover to the outer face and edges of the steel member of not less than 50 mm.

g.  The concrete casing extends the full length of the member and connections. Concrete is thoroughly compacted especially in areas under cleats, cap plates and beam soffits. Sufficient clearance is provided at all points so that the concrete can be efficiently worked around the steel elements.

h.  The casing is reinforced, using steel fabric complying with BS 4483, reference D98. Alternatively, steel reinforcement or wire of not less than 5 mm diameter or equivalent, complying with BS 4449 or BS 4482 may be used at a maximum spacing of 200 mm to form a cage of closed links and longitudinal bars. The reinforcement is so arranged as to pass through the centre of the concrete cover to the flanges. The minimum lap of the reinforcement, and the details of the links, should comply with BS 8110.

i.  The effective length $L_E$ of the cased section is limited to $40b_c$, $100b_c^2/d_c$ or $250\,r$ whichever is least,

where:

$b_c$  is the minimum width of solid casing within the depth of the steel section

$d_c$  is the minimum depth of solid casing within the width of the steel section

$r$  is the minimum radius of gyration of the steel section alone

Providing the above conditions are met, cased struts may be designed on the following basis.

(a) The radius of gyration, $r_y$, of the member about its axis in the plane of its web or webs should be taken as $0.2b_c$, but not more than $0.2(B + 150)$ mm, where $b_c$ is the minimum width of solid casing within the depth of the steel section and $B$ is the overall width of the steel flange or flanges. Where the radius of gyration of the steel section alone is greater than that of the composite section, the radius of gyration of the steel section alone may be used.

   The radius of gyration, $r_x$, of the member about its axis parallel to the planes of the flanges should be taken as that of the steel section alone.

(b) The compression resistance, $P_c$, of the cased section should be determined from:

$$P_c = \left( A_g + 0.45 \frac{A_c f_{cu}}{p_y} \right) p_c$$

but not greater than the short strut capacity given by:

$$P_{cs} = \left( A_g + 0.25 \frac{A_c f_{cu}}{p_y} \right) p_y$$

Where:

$A_c$ is the gross sectional area of the concrete, but neglecting any casing in excess of 75 mm from the overall dimensions of the steel section and neglecting any applied finish

$A_g$ is the gross sectional area of the steel member

$f_{cu}$ is the characteristic concrete cube strength at 28 days of the encasement but $\leq 40$ N/mm$^2$

$p_c$ is the compressive strength of the steel section

$p_y$ is the design strength of the steel but $\leq 355$ N/mm$^2$.

*Example 7.8.1. A 254 × 254 × 107 UC in grade S 275 steel is cased in reinforced concrete grade 30 and has a minimum cover of 50 mm making a 370 × 360 mm column overall dimensions. Calculate the load capacity assuming the following data: Effective height = 3 m; Area of steel section = 136 cm$^2$; B = 258.8 mm; $r_y$ (uncased) = 6.59 cm.*

## SOLUTION

Find $r_y$ cased:

$$r_y \text{ (cased)} = 0.2b_c = 0.2 \times 360 = 72 \text{ mm}$$

This should not be more than $0.2(B + 150)$ mm

$$0.2(B + 150) = 0.2(258.8 + 150) = 81.7 \text{ mm}$$

$$r_y \text{ (cased)} = 72 \text{ mm}$$

The flange thickness $(T)$ is 20.5 mm, therefore $p_y$ must be taken as 265 N/mm². 
    Check on maximum effective length $(L_E)$:

$$40b_c = \frac{40 \times 360}{10} = 1\ 440 \text{ cm}$$

$$100\frac{b_c^2}{d_c} = \frac{100 \times 360^2}{370 \times 10} = 3\ 502.7 \text{ cm}$$

$$250r = \frac{250 \times 65.7}{10} = 1\ 642.5 \text{ cm}$$

Clearly $L_E = 3.0$ m (300 cm) is within the limits specified in the code.
    Find slenderness ratio for cased strut:

$$\lambda = \frac{L_E}{r_y} = \frac{3.0 \times 100}{7.2} = 42.0$$

$$p_c \text{ (Table 24(c))} = 227 \text{ N/mm}^2$$

The compression resistance:

$$P_c = \left( A_g + 0.45 \frac{A_c f_{cu}}{p_y} \right) p_c$$

$$= \left( 136.0 + 0.45 \times \frac{\left( \dfrac{370 \times 360}{100} - 136.0 \right) \times 30}{265} \right) \times \frac{227}{10}$$

$$= 4\ 470 \text{ kN}$$

This should not be greater than:

$$P_{cs} = \left( A_g + 0.25\frac{A_c f_{cu}}{P_y} \right) P_y$$

$$= \left( 136.0 + 0.25 \times \frac{\left( \dfrac{370 \times 360}{100} - 136.0 \right) \times 30}{265} \right) \times \frac{265}{10}$$

$$= 4\,501 \text{ kN}$$

The capacity may then be taken as 4 470 kN

## 7.9. Eccentrically loaded struts

The preceding sections covered members subjected to axial load; in reality this situation occurs infrequently. The more common design situation involves axial load with moments applied about one or both axes.

Beams are generally connected to stanchions by brackets or cleats fixed to their flanges or webs (see Fig. 7.7). In §4.7.7 it is required that the load should be taken as acting at a distance from the face of the stanchion equal to 100 mm, or at the centre of the length of stiff bearing, whichever gives the greater eccentricity. (Eccentricity is the distance from the centre of the stanchion to the point where the load is taken as acting.) This type of design is known as 'simple construction' in BS 5950. Structures designed in this way must have sufficient lateral stability provided by either bracing or shear walls. For structures where continuity of the joints is assumed in the design, the moments on the stanchions are taken from the analysis of the frame.

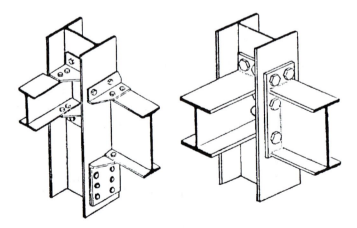

*Fig. 7.7.*

BS 5950 gives several formulae for the design of stanchions depending on the situation being considered. For the purposes of this book, it will be assumed that all sections are compact and that local buckling will not, therefore, govern the design. It is, however, important that the engineer recognises the effects of local buckling.

When an eccentric load acts on a stanchion, two main effects can be seen working towards failure. These are illustrated in Fig. 7.8(a) which shows the stanchion with an eccentric load; the additional forces shown in Fig. 7.8(b) do not affect equilibrium so that the effect on the stanchion is the same. A rearrangement of the forces into an axial load, Fig. 7.8(c), and a couple, Fig. 7.8(d), may be made. The division of eccentric loads into this form is the basis of the equations governing the design of stanchions or other members subjected to axial load and moments.

The design of compression members with moments is covered in §4.8.3. What is described as a more exact approach is given in §4.8.3.2, with the basic formulae given in the following form, covering members with moments about both axes:

$$\frac{F_c}{P_{cx}} + \frac{m_x M_x}{M_{cx}}\left(1 + 0.5\frac{F_c}{P_{cx}}\right) + 0.5\frac{m_{yx} M_y}{M_{cy}} \leq 1$$

$$\text{or } \frac{F_c}{P_{cy}} + \frac{m_{LT} M_{LT}}{M_b} + \frac{m_y M_y}{M_{cy}}\left(1 + \frac{F_c}{P_{cy}}\right) \leq 1$$

when there is lateral torsional buckling

$$\text{or } \frac{m_x M_x\left(1 + 0.5\dfrac{F_c}{P_{cx}}\right)}{M_{cx}\left(1 - \dfrac{F_c}{P_{cx}}\right)} + \frac{m_y M_y\left(1 + \dfrac{F_c}{P_{cy}}\right)}{M_{cy}\left(1 - \dfrac{F_c}{P_{cy}}\right)} \leq 1$$

when there is interactive buckling

In this equation, $m_{LT} M_{LT}$ and $m_y M_y$ are equivalent uniform moments (see Chapter 6); $M_{cx}$ and $M_{cy}$ are the moment capacities derived from §4.2.5, covering restrained beams,
where:

$F_c$ is the axial load

$P_c$ is the capacity or compression resistance of the member acting as a strut on the effective length of the member about the X–X and the Y–Y axes

$M_b$ is the moment capacity or buckling resistance moment of the section for lateral torsional buckling, as given in §4.3.

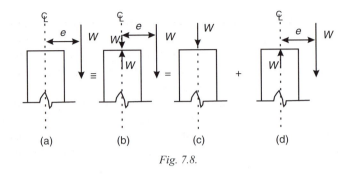

Fig. 7.8.

Note: BS 5950 gives alternative equations for moments in each single direction. If followed through, these can be derived from the equations given above, by setting the value of $M_x$ or $M_y = 0$.

These interaction equations use the equivalent uniform moment which may well be as little as 0.43 of the maximum moment. When a strut is relatively short the buckling values will be high, and a risk exists that the capacity of the member may be exceeded at the point of maximum moment. A further check is required to prevent this happening. The equations for this (§4.8.2.3), which must be satisfied at all points in the member, are:

$$M_x \leq M_{rx}$$
$$M_y \leq M_{ry}$$

$$\left( \frac{M_x}{M_{rx}} \right)^{z_1} + \left( \frac{M_y}{M_{ry}} \right)^{z_2} \leq 1$$

Where:

$z_1$ is a constant, taken as:    2.0 for I- or H-sections with equal flanges
2.0 for solid or hollow circular sections

5/3 for solid or hollow rectangular sections

1.0 for all other cases.

$z_2$ is a constant, taken as:    1.0 for I- and H-sections with equal flanges
2.0 for solid or hollow circular sections

5/3 for solid or hollow rectangular sections

1.0 for all other cases.

$M_{rx}$ and $M_{ry}$ are the reduced plastic moment capacities of the section ($p_y S$) in the presence of axial load (see section 5.4.4 of this book). The values of $M_{rx}$ and $M_{ry}$ may be calculated by reference to the equations given in the section books. The equations are based on the formulae given in Appendix B of *The Steel Skeleton* by Baker, Horne and Heyman.

In multi-storey frame situations, stanchion design occupies a significant part of the calculation and to save time a simplified approach is given. This short method may only be used for stanchions in simple multi-storey frames where moments are taken from notional eccentricities. When this method is employed, the following procedures may be adopted:

- All loads are applied at one time, i.e. pattern loading need not be considered.
- The bending moment introduced by the floor beams is shared by the stanchion lengths immediately above and below the floor under consideration. If the ratio of the stiffnesses of these stanchion lengths is less than 1.5, then the bending moment will be shared equally. If that ratio becomes more than 1.5, then the upper and lower lengths of the stanchion will share the total bending moment in proportion to their stiffnesses.
- The simplified method in §4.7.7 is to be used.

This formula is in the form:

$$\frac{F_c}{P_c} + \frac{M_x}{M_{bs}} + \frac{M_y}{p_y Z_y} \leq 1.0$$

where:

$P_c$ is the compression resistance $= p_c A_g$
$A_g$ is the gross cross-sectional area
$F_c$ is the axial force on the member
$p_c$ is the compressive strength taken from the appropriate part of BS 5950 Table 24
$M_{bs}$ is the buckling resistance moment capacity determined from $\lambda_{LT} = 0.5 \, L/r_y$
$M_x$ and $M_y$ are the maximum nominal moments on the member about the major and minor axes
$p_y$ is the design strength
$Z_y$ is the elastic section modulus about the minor axis.

It should be noted that the check is given without using the moment gradient correction ($m = 1$), so that no additional check is required on the local capacity at the ends of the member.

*Example 7.9.1. A 533 × 210 × 122 UB, grade S 275 steel, is subjected to a factored axial load of 1 410 kN. Calculate the reduced moment capacity of the section assuming that it is a short strut (λ < 17). Properties of the section to be taken from tables. It is assumed that the section capacity is not restricted by local buckling.*

## SOLUTION

In order to calculate the reduced moment capacity, the following steps must be taken:

(a) Calculate value of $\lambda$; in this case since it has already been given as less than 17, the full design value may be used.

(b) Check if $n\left(\dfrac{F}{A_g P_y}\right)$ is greater or less than the change formula value.

(c) Using the appropriate formula from section tables determined from Step (b) calculate the reduced moment.

Following these steps in this case:

$$\text{(b)} \quad n = 1\,410 \times \frac{1\,000}{\left(275 \times 155 \times 100\right)} = 0.331 \quad \therefore n < 0.410$$

(c) Using lower values of $n$ equation:

$S_r = K1 - K2 \times n^2$

$S_r = 3\,196 - 4\,760 \times (0.331)^2$

$S_r = 2\,674 \text{ cm}^3$

Moment $= 2\,674 \times 275/1\,000 = 735$ kNm

*Example 7.9.2. A 220 kN reaction from a beam, of which half is due to the imposed load, is supported at the top of a pin-jointed stanchion, 4 m long. Check if a 203 × 203 × 46 UC in grade S 275 steel is satisfactory. Assume that the beam to stanchion connection to be (a) to the flange and (b) to the web.*

The properties of the UC are:

| | | |
|---|---|---|
| A = 58.70 cm² | $Z_x$ = 450 cm³ | $S_x$ = 497 cm³ |
| D = 203.6 mm | $Z_y$ = 152 cm³ | |
| t = 7.2 mm | $r_y$ = 5.13 cm | |

## SOLUTION

### Case (a)

Effective length $(L_E)$ = actual length $(L)$ = 4 m

$$\frac{L_E}{r_y} = 4 \times \frac{100}{5.13} = 78.0$$

Eccentricity $= \dfrac{203.6}{2} + 100 = 201.8$ mm

Find factored value of the reaction:

DL $= 110 \times 1.4 = 154$ kN

IL $= 110 \times 1.6 = 176$ kN

Therefore the factored value of the reaction is 330 kN.

$$\text{Moment} = 330 \times \frac{201.8}{1\,000} = 66.6 \text{ kNm}$$

The calculations will be carried out using the rules for simple structures, §4.7.7.

The equation to be satisfied is in the form:

$$\frac{F_c}{P_c} + \frac{M_x}{M_{bs}} + \frac{M_y}{p_y \, Z_y} \leq 1.0$$

For axial load with $L_E / r_y = 78.0$,

$p_c$ (using Table 24(c)) = 165 N/mm².

The axial load capacity or compression resistance $= 165 \times \dfrac{58.7}{10}$

$$= 969 \text{ kN}$$

This case has bending about the X–X axis only.

$\therefore M_x = 66.6$ kNm

$M_{bs}$ is calculated using $\lambda_{LT} = 0.5L/r_y$ (§4.7.7)

$$\lambda_{LT} = 0.5 \times \frac{4 \times 100}{5.13} = 39.0 \text{ (Note in this particular case, } L_E = L.)$$

From Table 16, bending stress $p_b = 264$ N/mm²

Buckling resistance moment $(M_{bs}) = S_x p_b = 497 \times 264/10^3$

$M_{bs} = 131$ kNm

Substituting in the formula

$$\frac{330}{969} + \frac{66.6}{131} + 0$$

$$0.341 + 0.51 + 0 = 0.851$$

This is less than 1, therefore, the section is satisfactory.

### Case (b)

The axial load terms remain unchanged.

Eccentricity $= t/2 + 100 = 7.2/2 + 100 = 103.60$ mm

Moment $= 330 \times 103.6/10^3 = 34.2$ kNm

*The moment capacity about the y-axis* $(p_y Z_y) =$

$275 \times \dfrac{152}{10^3} = 41.8$ kNm

Case (b) has bending about the Y–Y axis only.

Substituting in the formula

$$\frac{330}{969} + 0 + \frac{34.2}{41.8}$$

$$0.341 + 0 + 0.818 = 1.159$$

This is greater than 1, therefore the section is not satisfactory.

*Example 7.9.3. A 406 × 178 × 74 UB, 4 m long, carries a factored axial load of 900 kN and a moment of 130 kNm on its stronger axis at the top. Assuming that the stanchion is pinned at each end, check if the section is adequate. Material used to be grade S 275 steel. Properties of section are to be taken from tables.*

### SOLUTION

This problem is to be solved using the more exact method given in §4.8.3.3.2. The equation for buckling is:

$$\frac{F_c}{P_{cx}} + \frac{m_x M_x}{M_{cx}}\left(1 + 0.5\frac{F_c}{P_{cx}}\right) + 0.5\frac{m_{yx} M_y}{M_{cy}} \le 1$$

or $\dfrac{F_c}{P_{cy}} + \dfrac{m_{LT} M_{LT}}{M_b} + \dfrac{m_y M_y}{M_{cy}}\left(1 + \dfrac{F_c}{P_{cy}}\right) \le 1$

when there is lateral torsional buckling

It should be noted that, as there is no moment about the *y*-axis, then the third term is 0.

Because $m_{LT}$ and $m_y$ will be less than 1, the end capacity must also be checked.

The equation for this is:

$$\left(\frac{M_x}{M_{rx}}\right)^{z_1} + \left(\frac{M_y}{M_{ry}}\right)^{z_2} \le 1$$

In this case, $z_1$ is 2 and $z_2$ is 1.

Before these equations can be used, the section must be checked to see if it is compact.

Looking at Table 11 of BS 5950 for webs generally, the limit is given as $40\varepsilon$ for all cases of a compact section.

The distance between fillets is 360.4 mm and the web thickness is 9.5 mm.

The flange thickness is 16 mm giving a design strength of 275 N/mm².

$$\therefore \varepsilon = 1.0$$

The *d/t* for the section is $360.4/9.5 = 37.9$

This is less than the limit ($40\varepsilon$) for any case for a web.

This is less than the limit for full compression over the whole section ($40\varepsilon$).

The limit for the outstand element of compression flange is $10\varepsilon$.

$$\text{The flange outstand} = \frac{179.5/2}{16} = 5.6$$

This limit is also satisfactory.

### Check for buckling

In this example, $M_y = 0$.

From Table 26 of BS 5950, $m_{LT}$ is 0.60 when there is a moment at one end only ($\beta = 0$).

Buckling moment $(m_{LT} M_x) = 0.60 \times 130 = 78$ kNm

The value of $\lambda$ is $4 \times 100/4.04 = 99.0$

$p_c = 142$ N/mm²

$P_c = 142 \times 94.5/10 = 1\,342$ kN

The lateral torsional buckling resistance $M_{LT}$ is based on $\lambda_{LT} = uv\lambda\sqrt{\beta_w}$.

Since the section is compact, the value of $\beta_w = 1.0$.

$u = 0.882$ from section tables.

$v$ is taken from BS 5950 Table 19 based on $\lambda/x$, where $x$ is taken from section tables $= 27.6$.

$$\lambda/x = 99/27.6 = 3.59 \quad \therefore v = 0.89$$

$$\lambda_{LT} = 0.882 \times 0.89 \times 99 = 78$$

$$p_b = 169 \text{ N/mm}^2$$

$$M_b = 169 \times 1\,501/10^3 = 254 \text{ kNm}$$

$$M_{cx} = 275 \times 1\,501/10^3 = 414 \text{ kNm}$$

Substituting in the formulae:

$$\frac{900}{1\,342} + \frac{78}{413}\left(1 + 0.5\frac{900}{1\,342}\right) = 0.671 + 0.252 = 0.923$$

$$\frac{900}{1\,342} + \frac{78}{254} = 0.671 + 0.307 = 0.978$$

The section is satisfactory in bending and buckling, but the end capacity must now be checked.

$$n = \frac{F}{A_g\,p_y} = \frac{900 \times 10}{94.5 \times 275} = 0.346$$

The reduced plastic modulus $= K1 - K2\,n^2 =$
$1\,504 - (2\,340 \times (0.346)^2) = 1\,221 \text{ cm}^3$

Plastic moment of resistance $= 275 \times 1\,221/10^3 = 336 \text{ kNm}$

$$\left(\frac{130}{336}\right)^2 + 0 = 0.15$$

This is less than 1, and therefore the section is satisfactory for both buckling and end capacity.

*Example 7.9.4. A 152 × 152 × 23 UC grade S 275 steel acts as a 6 m long stanchion with both ends fixed in position and direction. It carries a vertical axial imposed load of 40 kN, a dead load of 20 kN and a bending moment, at one end, due to the wind of 20 kNm, about its stronger axis. Check if the section is satisfactory. Properties of section are to be taken from tables.*

## SOLUTION

This example illustrates the method of combining wind loads with dead and imposed loads. The following cases should be considered, although experience may well show which need to be checked in everyday design.

From Table 2 of BS 5950:

(a)  IL + DL

Factors to be used are: IL =1.6, DL = 1.4

(b)  WL + DL

Factors to be used are: WL = 1.4, DL = 1.4

(c)  IL + DL + WL

Factors to be used are: IL = 1.2, DL = 1.2, WL = 1.2

The stanchion must be checked for the following loads, taking each case in turn:

Case (a)  Axial load = 40 × 1.6 + 20 × 1.4 = 92 kN

Case (b)  Axial load = 20 × 1.4 = 28 kN

Moment  = 20 × 1.4 = 28 kNm

Case (c)  Axial load = 40 × 1.2 + 20 × 1.2 = 72 kN

Moment 20 × 1.2 = 24 kNm

*Case (a)*

$$L_E = 0.7 \times 6 = 4.2 \text{ m}, \quad r_y = 3.70 \text{ cm.}$$

$$\lambda = \frac{L_E}{r_y} = \frac{4.2 \times 100}{3.70} = 114$$

Using BS 5950 Table 24(c) and a design stress, $p_y$, of 275 N/mm$^2$:

$$p_c = 105 \text{ N/mm}^2$$

$$P_c = A_g p_c = \frac{29.2 \times 105}{10} = 307 \text{ kN}$$

This is greater than the applied load (92 kN), therefore the section is adequate for case (a).

## Case (b)

Moment for buckling calculation is based on a full reversal of moment, therefore the value of $\beta$ for BS 5950 Table 26 is $-1$ giving a value of $m_{LT} = 0.40$. The buckling moment is $0.40 \times 28 = 11.2$ kNm.

Calculate the buckling moment capacity ($M_b$):

$\lambda = 114$, $u = 0.840$, $x = 20.4$ (from section tables)

$$\frac{\lambda}{x} = \frac{114}{20.7} = 5.5$$

$\therefore v = 0.79$ (from BS 5950 Table 19)

$$\lambda_{LT} = uv\lambda\sqrt{\beta_w} = 0.84 \times 0.79 \times 114 \times 1 = 76$$

$p_b = 175$ N/mm$^2$ (from Table 16)

$$M_b = \frac{184 \times 175}{10^3} = 32.2 \text{ kNm}$$

The formula to be used is $\dfrac{F_c}{P_c} + \dfrac{M_x}{M_{bs}} + \dfrac{M_y}{M_{bs}} \leq 1.0$  $M_y$ is 0 so the third term disappears.

$$\frac{28}{307} + \frac{11.2}{32.2} = 0.091 + 0.348 = 0.439$$

This is less than 1.0 and the section is, therefore, satisfactory for this condition.

## Case (c)

$$F_c = 72 \text{ kN}$$

$p_{cy}$ is derived using the failure mode about the $y$-axis.

$$\lambda_y = \frac{L_E}{r_y} = \frac{4.2 \times 100}{3.70} = 114$$

$$\therefore p_{cy} = 105 \text{ N/mm}^2$$

$$P_{cy} = 105 \times \frac{29.2}{10} = 307 \text{ kN}$$

Assuming that the moment is divided equally between the top and bottom of the member, due to full fixity, then the equivalent uniform moment, $m_{LT} M_{LT} = 0.40 \times 24 = 9.6$ kNm

Substituting in the lateral torsional formula:

$$\frac{72}{307} + \frac{9.6}{32} = 0.235 + 0.297 = 0.532$$

As this is less than 1.0, the section is adequate for buckling due to axial load and bending.

*Check the end capacity*

$$n = \frac{72 \times 10}{29.2 \times 275} = 0.09$$

Reduced plastic modulus $(S_r) = K1 - K2n^2$

$$M_{rx} = p_y S_r = \frac{275(184 - 364(0.09)^2)}{10^3} = 49.8 \text{ kNm}$$

Applied moment = 24 kNm.
The end capacity is, therefore, satisfactory.

## 7.10. Stanchion bases

When the load on a stanchion is concentric, the force is transmitted to the foundation by means of a steel baseplate. Such bases, known also as slab bases, are designed by calculating the bending moments about the edges of the stanchion profile. In cases where the projection is large or when moments are applied, the baseplate is stiffened by the use of vertical plates or stiffeners. Examples are shown in Fig. 7.9, covering both types of bases.

Stanchions are normally supported on reinforced concrete foundations with bolts which provide for fixing during erection and resist any tension forces which may be present due to moments or applied tension. Erection will normally take place by lowering the stanchion and its base over the holding down bolts onto packs, which are pre-levelled and up to 50 mm thick. The bolts are used to enable the stanchion to be plumbed into the vertical position. When sufficient permanent structure has been erected to ensure that the stanchion is held permanently in place then a grout is placed between the underside of the baseplate and the top of the foundation.

BS 5950: Part 2 specifies the type of grout to be employed as follows:

(a) For a gap less than 25 mm, a neat Portland cement grout poured under a suitable head.
(b) For gaps between 25 mm and 50 mm, a fluid cement mortar not less than 1:1 Portland cement: sand poured under a suitable head and tamped.
(c) For gaps greater than 50 mm, a 1:2 Portland cement:fine aggregate mortar, well rammed against a suitable stop board.

The use of special grouts is also permitted; they may be made by using admixtures to prevent shrinkage or expanding grouts or resin-based grouts. On completion of grouting and its setting, temporary packs should be removed if possible; frequently, however, they have to be left in, and must,

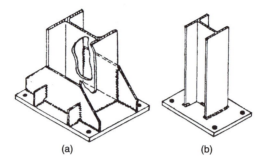

(a)                                      (b)

*Fig. 7.9.*

therefore, be thoroughly covered with grout or concrete. When bases exceed 600 mm square, it is regarded as good practice to drill two holes at convenient positions towards the centre of the base to enable the grout to be placed and checked easily.

The design of baseplates to BS 5950 is controlled by §4.13 which requires that the baseplates should be of adequate size, stiffness and strength to transmit the load from the stanchion to the concrete. The bearing strength of the concrete is taken as $0.6f_{cu}$, where $f_{cu}$ is the characteristic concrete strength at 28 days.

The minimum baseplate thickness is determined on the basis that the baseplate cantilevers from the face of the section are as shown in 7.10. The ineffective areas may be ignored in the design process.

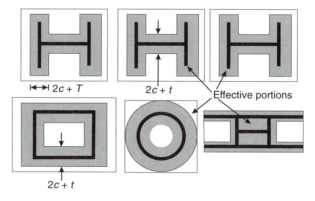

*Fig. 7.10.*

This gives certain formula for the determination of the baseplate thickness, using given formula. These are based on the effective area of the baseplate as shown in Fig. 7.10.

The bearing pressure under the effective areas must be less than $0.6f_{cu}$, where $f_{cu}$ is the characteristic strength of the concrete.

The value of $c$ is the same from all faces of the steel member.

The thickness of the baseplate $t_p$ is to be not less than:

$$t_p = c\left[\frac{3w}{p_{yp}}\right]^{0.5}$$

Where:

$c$ is the largest distance from the face of the column to the edge of the effective area

$p_{yp}$ is the design strength of the baseplate

$w$ is the pressure under the baseplate assumed to be uniform.

*Example 7.10.1. Design a baseplate, in grade S 275 steel, to a 305 × 305 × 198 UC carrying a factored axial load of 5 350 kN. The reinforced concrete base supporting the baseplate is to be grade 30 concrete to BS 8110.*

The overall size of the section is $D = 339.9$ mm and $B = 314.5$ mm. These figures will be rounded to 340.0 mm and 315.0 mm, respectively. The baseplate design strength, $p_{yp}$, assuming the plate will be greater than 40 mm, is taken as 255 N/mm².

This example is one where it is probably safer to keep to mm units throughout.

### SOLUTION

Bearing stress $= 0.6f_{cu} = 0.6 \times 30 = 18$ N/mm²

Effective area of baseplate required:

$$5\,350 \times \frac{10^3}{18} = 297\,222 \text{ mm}^2$$

In determining the shape of the effective area there are two possibilities, shown in Fig. 7.11(a) and (b). In the first case, the effective area is an H-shape following the profile of the section; in the second it is a rectangle.

In order to find the minimum projection required in the first case, it is necessary to solve a quadratic equation. The area is given by:

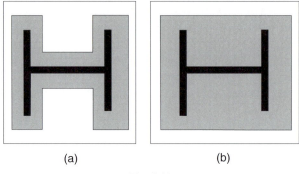

(a)                                    (b)

Fig. 7.11.

$2(B + 2c)(T + 2c) + (D - 2T - 2c)(t + 2c)$

$= 2BT + 4cB + 4cT + 8c^2 + Dt + 2cD - 2Tt - 2Tc - 2ct - 4c^2$

$= 2BT + 4cB + 2cT + Dt + 2cD - 2Tt - 2ct + 4c^2$

$= (2BT + Dt - 2Tt) + c(4B + 2T + 2D - 2t) + 4c^2$

For this example:

$B = 315$ mm, $D = 340$ mm, $T = 31.4$ mm, and $t = 19.1$ mm.

This gives the following equation:

$(2 \times 315 \times 31.4 + 340 \times 19.1 - 2 \times 31.4 \times 19.1)$
$+ c(4 \times 315 + 2 \times 31.4 + 2 \times 340 - 2 \times 19.1) + 4c^2 = 297\,222$ mm$^2$

$\therefore (19\,782 + 6\,494 - 1\,199) + c(1\,260 + 63 + 680 - 38.2) + 4c^2$
$= 297\,222$ mm$^2$

$\therefore -272\,154 + 1\,285c + 4c^2 = 0$

This is a quadratic equation, the solution of which $c = 146$ mm.

The depth between the inner faces of the flanges is $340 - 2 \times 31.4 = 277$ mm.

The space required to take this value of $c$ is $146 \times 2 = 292$ mm.

This is clearly not acceptable as the areas under the flanges overlap.

When this happens, BS 5950 fails to give specific instructions, but it must be assumed that a rectangular effective area should be used. The best solution is, therefore, to use an area with approximately the same projection on all faces; try a baseplate with an effective area 500 mm × 470 mm = 235 000 mm$^2$.

The actual bearing pressure is $5\,350 \times 1\,000/297\,222 = 18$ N/mm$^2$.

The thickness is determined from the maximum projection of the plate; this is taken assuming the column is in the centre of the baseplate, giving the following projections:

$$\frac{(500 - 340)}{2} = 80 \text{ mm}$$

$$\text{or} \quad \frac{(470 - 315)}{2} = 78 \text{ mm}$$

Design on a projection of 80 mm and a bearing pressure of 18 N/mm$^2$.

$$t_p = 80 \left( 3 \times \frac{18}{275} \right)^{0.5} = 135.5 \text{ mm}$$

It would be normal to use a plate 40 mm thick and 500 × 500 mm.

Notes: Unless a very deep section is used it is advisable to make the baseplates, or slab bases, square in order to eliminate fabrication errors when attaching the baseplate to the section.

It is also advisable to ensure that the plate has adequate thickness. This was covered in earlier versions of BS 5950 by requiring the plate to be the same thickness as the flanges of the supported column. This advice, used with common sense, is still valid.

## 7.11. Stanchions in multi-storey buildings

Mention has already been made of the procedures for design stanchions in simple multi-storey frames, i.e. frames braced against sidesway and with joints designed as simple pinned connections. The method given in §4.7.7 allows for the rapid design of such elements, without the need to carry out the checks on end capacity.

*Example 7.11.1. A stanchion, 4.8 m long, consists of a 254 × 254 × 73 UC, and is loaded as shown in Fig. 7.12. The factored loads shown are transmitted to the stanchion by floor beams. In addition, there is a factored axial load of 930 kN. The stanchion lengths for the upper floors are 4.5 m long and consists of a 203 × 203 × 71 UC. (The splice between the stanchion lengths is assumed to be capable of carrying a substantial moment.) Test the suitability of the 254 × 254 × 73 UC, assuming that this stanchion length has substantial beam connections at both ends. The steel is to be grade S 275. The design strength for steel (grade S 275 <16 mm thick) is 275 N/mm².*

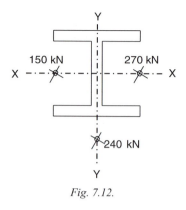

150 kN    270 kN

240 kN

Fig. 7.12.

## SOLUTION

First find the stiffness of the sections ($I/L$ since $E$ is constant).

### X–X axis

$L$ of 203 × 203 × 71 UC = 4.5 m

$L$ of 254 × 254 × 73 UC = 4.8 m

$I_x$ of 203 × 203 × 71 UC = 7 618 cm⁴

$I_x$ of 254 × 254 × 73 UC = 11 410 mm⁴

Stiffness of 203 × 203 × 71 UC = $7618/(4.5 \times 100)$ = 16.93 cm³

Stiffness of 254 × 254 × 73 UC = $11410/(4.8 \times 100)$ = 23.77 cm³

Ratio of the two stiffnesses = 23.77/16.93 = 1.4

which is less than 1.5.

### Y–Y axis

$I_y$ of 203 × 203 × 71 UC = 2 537 cm⁴

$I_y$ of 254 × 254 × 73 UC = 3 908 cm⁴

Stiffness of 203 × 203 × 71 UC = $2537/(4.5 \times 100)$ = 5.64 cm³

Stiffness of 254 × 254 × 73 UC = $3908/(4.8 \times 100)$ = 8.14 cm³

Ratio of the two stiffnesses = 8.14/5.64 = 1.44

which is less than 1.5.

In neither case does the ratio of the stiffnesses exceed 1.5, therefore the bending moment may be assumed to be divided equally between the two stanchion lengths.

Total vertical factored load on 254 × 254 × 73 UC:

$$930 + 240 + 150 + 270 = 1\,590$$

$$L_E = 0.7L = 0.7 \times 4.8 = 3.36 \text{ m}$$

$$\lambda = L_E / r_y = 3.36 \times 100/6.48 = 52$$

From BS 5950 Table 24(c), for a design strength of 275 N/mm², $p_c = 217$ N/mm².

Eccentricity in X–X direction = $\frac{1}{2}$ section depth + 100 mm.

$$M_x = 240 \frac{\left( \dfrac{254}{2} + 100 \right)}{10^3} = 54.48 \text{ kNm}$$

Eccentricity about Y–Y axis = $\frac{1}{2}$ web thickness + 100 mm.

$$M_y = (270 - 150) \frac{\left( \dfrac{8.6}{2} + 100 \right)}{10^3} = 12.516 \text{ kNm}$$

The overall strength is checked using the formula for the simplified approach in §4.7.7:

$$\frac{F_c}{P_c} + \frac{M_x}{M_{bs}} + \frac{M_y}{p_y Z_y} \le 1$$

where:

$F_c$ = axial load = 1 590 kN

$P_c$ = compression resistance of the member = $p_c A_g = 217 \times 93.1/10$ = 2 020 kN

$A_g$ = gross area of the section = 93.1 cm²

$p_c$ = compressive strength = 217 N/mm² from Table 24(c) based on $\lambda = 52$.

$M_x$ = Moment about X–X axis divided equally between the stanchion lengths = 54.48/2 = 27.24 kNm

$M_y$ = Moment about Y–Y axis divided equally between the stanchion lengths = 12.516/2 = 6.258 kNm

$M_{bs}$ = buckling moment resistance for simple design calculated from $p_b S_x$ where $p_b$ is taken from BS 5950 Table 16, assuming $\lambda_{LT} = \frac{1}{2}L/r_y$.

$$\lambda_{LT} = \frac{1}{2}\frac{4.8 \times 100}{6.48} = 37$$

$$\therefore \ p_b = 268 \ \text{N}/\text{mm}^2$$

$$M_{bs} = p_b S_x$$

$$M_{bs} = 268 \times \frac{992}{10^3} = 266 \ \text{kNm}$$

Elastic modulus about the Y–Y axis = 307.0 cm³.

The moment capacity about the $y$-axis = $p_y Z_y = 275 \times 307/10^3$
= 84.4 kNm.

Substituting these values in the equation:

$$\frac{1590}{2020} + \frac{27.24}{266} + \frac{6.258}{84.4}$$
$$= \ 0.787 + 0.102 + 0.075$$
$$= \ 0.964$$

The section is therefore satisfactory for overall buckling.

The moment gradient factor, $m$, has been taken as 1 (§4.7.7), the local capacity will not be exceeded, if $m$ is taken as 1.

*Example 7.11.2. Supposing the upper stanchion in example 7.11.1 was a 203 × 203 × 60 UC instead of a 203 × 203 × 71 UC and assuming all other data to be the same, test the suitability of the 254 × 254 × 73 UC.*

## SOLUTION

Following the steps taken in example 7.11.1, determine the relative stiffnesses.

### X–X axis

Stiffness of 203 × 203 × 60 UC = $6125/(4.5 \times 100) = 13.61$ cm³
Stiffness of 254 × 254 × 73 UC = as before = 23.77 cm³
Ratio of stiffnesses = 23.77/13.61 = 1.75
This is greater than 1.5. Therefore the moments are to be distributed in the ratio of the section stiffnesses.

### Y–Y axis

Stiffness of $203 \times 203 \times 60$ UC $= 2\,065 / (4.5 \times 100) = 4.59$ cm$^3$
Stiffness of $254 \times 254 \times 73$ UC $=$ as before $= 8.14$ cm$^3$
Ratio of stiffnesses $= 8.14/4.59 = 1.77$

This is greater than 1.5. Therefore the moments are to be distributed in the ratio of the section stiffnesses.

Moments to be used for checking section.

### X–X axis

$$54.480 \times \left[ \frac{23.77}{(23.77 + 13.61)} \right] = 34.6 \text{ kNm}$$

(This may also be shown to be moment $\times$ ratio/(1 + ratio) $= 54.48 \times 1.75/2.75$)

### Y–Y axis

$$12.516 \times \left[ \frac{8.14}{(8.14 + 4.59)} \right] = 8.0 \text{ kNm}$$

$$\left( \text{or } 12.516 \times \frac{1.77}{2.77} \right)$$

Except for these moments, all the terms in the expression at the end of example 7.11.1 remain unchanged.

$$\frac{1590}{2\,020} + \frac{34.6}{266} + \frac{8.0}{84.4} =$$

$$0.787 + 0.130 + 0.095 = 1.012$$

This is greater than unity indicating that the section is unsatisfactory. The results of this calculation act as a reminder to the engineer that he must always consider structures as an entity. He must also recognise the effect which constituent parts may have on each other.

*Example 7.11.3. In a five-storey building, for storage purposes, the external stanchions, which have pinned bases, receive minor axis factored reactions of 49 kN from both sides of the web while the major axis factored reaction is 171 kN. The first storey stanchion is a cased grade S 275, 152 × 152 × 37 UC with overall dimensions of 270 × 260 mm. The storey height for all floors is 3.0 m except for the ground-to-first storey height, which is 3.3 m. Check if a grade S 275, cased, 203 × 203 × 46 UC with overall dimensions of 310 × 310 mm would satisfy the requirements of BS 5950 when used for the ground floor stanchion. The characteristic concrete cube strength at 28 days of the concrete may be assumed to be 30 N/mm$^2$.*

## SOLUTION

As the building is used for storage purposes, no reduction may be made to the imposed load.

Total axial load $= F_c = 5[171 + (2 \times 49)] = 5 \times 269 = 1\,345$ kN

$$e_x = \frac{203.2}{2} + 100 = 201.6 \text{ mm}$$

Bending moment (BM) induced at first floor $= M_x = 171 \times 201.6/10^3 = 34.5$ kNm

The bending moment should be shared between the stanchion lengths above and below the first floor.

Stiffness of $152 \times 152 \times 37$ UC $= 2\,210/(3.0 \times 100) = 7.37$ cm³

Stiffness of $203 \times 203 \times 46$ UC $= 4\,568/(3.3 \times 100) = 13.84$ cm³

Ratio of stiffnesses $= 13.84/7.37 = 1.88$

This is greater than 1.5, so the bending moment is going to be shared in proportion to the ratio of the stiffnesses.

Proportion of BM taken by the ground floor stanchion

$$= \left[\frac{13.84}{(13.84 + 7.37)}\right] \times 34.5 = 0.652 \times 34.5 = 22.51 \text{ kNm}$$

BS 5950 permits the concrete casing to be taken into account by increasing the stiffness of the section and sharing the axial load between the steel and concrete casing.

The radius of gyration of the section is taken as the greater of the radius of gyration of the uncased section or $0.2b_c$, where $b_c$ is the width of the casing but not greater than $0.2(B + 150)$ mm, where $B$ is the width of the section.

$r = 0.2b = 0.2 \times 310 = 62$ mm

$r = 0.2(B + 150) = 0.2(203.2 + 150) = 70.6$ mm

$r$ of the uncased section $= 5.13$ cm

Use the value for the cased section (62 mm)

$L_E = 0.85L = 0.85 \times 3.3 = 2.805$ m

$\lambda = L_E/r_y$ cased $= 2.805 \times 10^3/62 = 45.30$

from Table 24(c), $p_c = 229$ N/mm².

Two checks are required on this section:

(a) a check on the capacity of the section (§4.14.2) for which the equation is:

$$\frac{F_c}{P_{cs}} + \frac{M_x}{M_{cx}} + \frac{M_y}{M_{cy}} \leq 1$$

(b) a buckling resistance check for which the equation is:

$$\frac{F_c}{P_{cy}} + \frac{m_{LT}\,M_{LT}}{M_{bs}} + \frac{m_y\,M_y}{p_y\,Z_y} \leq 1$$

In these expressions, the following values should be taken:-

$F_c$ = axial load = 1 345 kN

$P_{cs}$ = short strut capacity of the section = $(A_g + 0.25 f_{cu}\,A_c/p_y\,)\,p_y$ (see also §7.8).

$A_g$ is the gross sectional area of the steel

$A_c$ is the gross sectional area of the concrete (see §4.14.2).

$P_{cs}$ = $(58.7 \times 100 + 0.25 \times 30 \times (310 \times 310 - 58.7 \times 100)/275) \times 275/10^3$ = 2 291 kN

$M_x$ = maximum moment about the X–X axis = 22.51 kNm

$M_{cx}$ = major axis moment capacity of the section assuming no help from the casing = $p_y S_x$ = $275 \times 497/10^3$ = 136.7 kNm

$M_{cy}$ = Minor axis moment capacity about Y–Y axis assuming no help from the casing. In this case the limiting value will be 1.5 $p_y Z_y$ (§4.2.5.1), i.e. the elastic moment capacity because the value of $Z_y$ (152 cm³) is less than $S_y/1.5$, i.e. 230/1.5 = 153 cm³.

$M_{cy}$ = $1.5 \times 275 \times 152/10^3$ = 62.7 kNm

$P_c$ = axial load capacity of the section allowing for buckling

= $(A_g + 0.45 f_{cu}\,A_c p_y)p_c$

= $(58.7 \times 100 + 0.45 \times 30 \times (310 \times 310 - 58.7 \times 100)/275) \times 229/10^3$

= 2 358 kN

$$= (58.7 \times 100 + 0.45 \times 30 \times (310 \times 310 - 58.7 \times 100)/275) \times 229/10^3$$

$$= 2\ 358\ \text{kN}$$

$m_{LT}$ = equivalent uniform moment factor which for this case will be taken as 0.6 assuming the maximum moment at one end, and zero at the other.

$M_{LT}$ = the maximum moment in the column length.

$M_{bs}$ = buckling resistance moment calculated as follows:

$$\lambda_{LT} = uv\lambda\sqrt{\beta_w}$$

$u = 0.847$, from section properties tables

$$\lambda = 3.3 \times 10^3/62 = 53$$

$v$ = slenderness factor from BS 5950 Table 19 ($\lambda/x = 53/17.7 = 2.99$)

$\therefore v = 0.91$

$\beta_w = 1.0$ for class 1 and 2 cross-sections

$$\lambda_{LT} = 0.847 \times 0.91 \times 53 \times 1.0 = 41$$

From BS 5950 Table 16, $p_b = 260\ \text{N/mm}^2$

$$M_{bs} = p_b S_x = 260 \times 497/10^3 = 129\ \text{kNm}$$

Substituting in the main equations:

(a) $\dfrac{1\ 345}{2\ 241} + \dfrac{22.51}{136.7} + 0 = 0.600 + 0.165 + 0 = 0.765$

(b) $\dfrac{1\ 345}{2\ 358} + \dfrac{0.6 \times 22.46}{129} + 0 = 0.570 + 0.104 + 0 = 0.674$

The section is, therefore, satisfactory.

*Example 7.11.4. An internal stanchion in a six-storey office building for general use is loaded in the following manner:*

|  | Dead load | | Imposed load | |
|---|---|---|---|---|
|  | Unfactored | Factored | Unfactored | Factored |
| *At roof level:* | | | | |
| Minor axis reaction from both sides of web | 10 | 14 | 0 | 0 |
| Major axis reaction from left of flange | 35 | 49 | 15 | 24 |
| Major axis reaction from right of flange | 50 | 70 | 25 | 40 |
| *At any other floor level:* | | | | |
| Minor axis reaction from one side of web | 10 | 14 | 0 | 0 |
| Minor axis reaction from the other side | 20 | 28 | 0 | 0 |
| Major axis reaction from left of flange | 50 | 70 | 20 | 32 |
| Major axis reaction from right of flange | 110 | 154 | 60 | 96 |

*The stanchion, which is cased in lightweight casing, such as plaster board, or similar, has a pinned base and a splice just above the third floor level. The steel used for the upper storeys is a 203 × 203 × 46 UC and the one used for the lower storeys is a 254 × 254 × 89 UC. Both sections are grade S 275 steel.*

*The storey height for all floors is 3.5 m with an additional length of 0.5 m below ground level.*

*Check the adequacy of both steel sections, assuming that the self-weight of each steel stanchion and casing is 5 kN (7 kN factored load).*

## SOLUTION

BS 6399 –1:1996 gives Table 7.1 for reduction in total distributed imposed floor loads in multi-storey buildings.

BS 6399 also states that no reduction shall be made for the following types of loading:

(a) Any loads that have been specifically determined from a knowledge of the proposed use of the structure.
(b) Loads due to plant or machinery.
(c) Loads due to storage.
(d) Roofs should not be counted as floors and their imposed loads reduced.

*BS 6399 Table 7.1.*

| Number of floors carried by member under consideration | Reduction in total distributed imposed load on all floors carried by the member under consideration. |
|---|---|
| | % |
| 1 | 0 |
| 2 | 10 |
| 3 | 20 |
| 4 | 30 |
| 5 to 10 | 40 |
| Over 10 | 50 maximum |

Since in this example, it is an office building of general use, reduction of the imposed load is applicable.

A typical calculation sheet for the stanchion is shown in Fig. 7.13. Check for the adequacy of the 203 × 203 × 46 UC at third-floor level.

Using the rules for simple columns:

Axial load = 994 kN

$L_E = 0.7 \times 3.5 = 2.45$ m

$L_E/r_y \ (\lambda) = 2.45 \times 100/5.13 = 48$

$p_c$ (using BS 5950 Table 24(c)) = 224 N/mm²

$P_c = p_c \, A_g = 224 \times 58.7/10 = 1\ 315$ kN

$\lambda_{LT} = \dfrac{1}{2}\dfrac{L}{r_y} = \dfrac{1}{2}\dfrac{3.5 \times 10}{5.13} = 34.1$ \hfill (§4.7.7)

$p_b = 275$ N/mm²

$M_{bs} = 275 \times 497/10^3 = 137$ kNm

$p_y Z_y = 275 \times 152/10^3 = 41.8$ kNm

$e_x = 203.2/2 + 100 = 201.6$ mm

$M_x = \dfrac{201.6\left[(154 + 96) - (70 + 32)\right]}{2 \times 10^3} = 14.9$ kNm

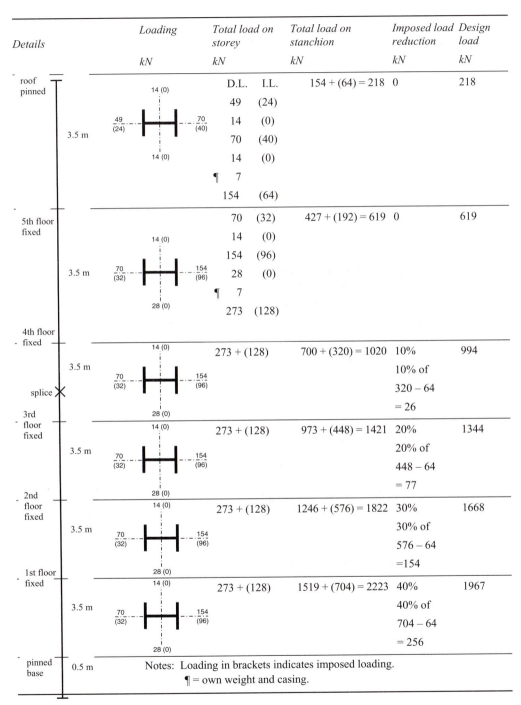

| Details | | Loading kN | Total load on storey kN | | Total load on stanchion kN | Imposed load reduction kN | Design load kN |
|---|---|---|---|---|---|---|---|
| roof pinned | | 14 (0) | D.L. | I.L. | 154 + (64) = 218 | 0 | 218 |
| | 3.5 m | $\frac{49}{(24)}$   $\frac{70}{(40)}$ | 49 | (24) | | | |
| | | | 14 | (0) | | | |
| | | | 70 | (40) | | | |
| | | 14 (0) | 14 | (0) | | | |
| | | | ¶ 7 | | | | |
| | | | 154 | (64) | | | |
| 5th floor fixed | | 14 (0) | 70 | (32) | 427 + (192) = 619 | 0 | 619 |
| | | | 14 | (0) | | | |
| | | | 154 | (96) | | | |
| | 3.5 m | $\frac{70}{(32)}$   $\frac{154}{(96)}$ | 28 | (0) | | | |
| | | 28 (0) | ¶ 7 | | | | |
| | | | 273 | (128) | | | |
| 4th floor fixed | 3.5 m | 14 (0) | 273 + (128) | | 700 + (320) = 1020 | 10% | 994 |
| | | $\frac{70}{(32)}$   $\frac{154}{(96)}$ | | | | 10% of | |
| splice | | | | | | 320 − 64 | |
| 3rd floor fixed | | 28 (0) | | | | = 26 | |
| | 3.5 m | 14 (0) | 273 + (128) | | 973 + (448) = 1421 | 20% | 1344 |
| | | $\frac{70}{(32)}$   $\frac{154}{(96)}$ | | | | 20% of | |
| | | | | | | 448 − 64 | |
| 2nd floor fixed | | 28 (0) | | | | = 77 | |
| | 3.5 m | 14 (0) | 273 + (128) | | 1246 + (576) = 1822 | 30% | 1668 |
| | | $\frac{70}{(32)}$   $\frac{154}{(96)}$ | | | | 30% of | |
| | | | | | | 576 − 64 | |
| 1st floor fixed | | 28 (0) | | | | =154 | |
| | 3.5 m | 14 (0) | 273 + (128) | | 1519 + (704) = 2223 | 40% | 1967 |
| | | $\frac{70}{(32)}$   $\frac{154}{(96)}$ | | | | 40% of | |
| | | | | | | 704 − 64 | |
| | | 28 (0) | | | | = 256 | |
| pinned base | 0.5 m | Notes: Loading in brackets indicates imposed loading.  ¶ = own weight and casing. | | | | | |

*Fig. 7.13.*

$$e_y = 7.2/2 + 100 = 103.6 \text{ mm}$$

$$M_y = \frac{103.6 \times (28 - 14)}{2 \times 10^3} = 0.725 \text{ kNm}$$

From §4.7.7:

$$\frac{F_c}{P_c} + \frac{M_x}{M_{bs}} + \frac{M_y}{p_y Z_y} \leq 1$$

Substituting in this equation:

$$\frac{994}{1315} + \frac{14.9}{137.0} + \frac{0.725}{41.8} =$$

$$0.756 + 0.109 + 0.018 = 0.883$$

This section meets the code requirements.

Check the adequacy of 254 × 254 × 89 UC for the lower length from ground to first floor.

Since T = 17.3 mm which is greater than 16 mm, therefore $p_y = 265 \text{ N/mm}^2$

Axial load = 1 967 kN

$$L_E = 0.85 \, L = 0.85 \times 4.0 = 3.40 \text{ m}$$

$$\lambda = L_E / r_y = 3.4 \times 10^2 / 6.55 = 52$$

From BS 5950 Table 24(c), $p_c = 210 \text{ N/mm}^2$

$P_c$ (compressive resistance of column) $= 210 \times 113/10 = 2 \, 373 \text{ kN}$

For bending $\lambda_{LT} = \dfrac{1}{2} \dfrac{L}{r_y} = \dfrac{1}{2} \dfrac{4 \times 10}{6.55} = 30.53$

$p_b = 265 \text{ N/mm}^2$

$M_{bs} = 265 \times 1224/10^3 = 324 \text{ kNm}$

$p_y Z_y = 265 \times 379/10^3 = 100.4 \text{ kNm}$

$e_x = 260.3/2 + 100 = 230.2 \text{ mm}$

$$M_x = \frac{230.2[(154 + 96) - (70 + 32)]}{2 \times 10^3} = 17.035 \text{ kNm}$$

$e_y = 10.3/2 + 100 = 105.15$ mm

$$M_y = \frac{105.15 \times (28 - 14)}{2 \times 10^3} = 0.736 \text{ kNm}$$

Substituting in the equation:

$$\frac{1967}{2373} + \frac{17.035}{324} + \frac{0.736}{100.4} =$$

$$0.829 + 0.053 + 0.007 = 0.889$$

Both sections are adequate.

## 7.12. Stanchion splices

Fig. 7.14 shows various ways of forming a stanchion splice.

Fig. 7.14(a) shows a splice for equal sections, and Fig. 7.14(b) for different sections but with the same serial size. This latter detail is not commonly used in Ireland although some British publications advocate it.

Where the serial size is different, as in Fig. 7.14(c) and Fig. 7.14(d), web cleats and a division plate are provided to give a better load dispersal.

The following rules are not extracts from codes but are empirical rules which give good results in practice.

- The projection of the flange plate beyond the end of the members to be at least equal to the upper flange width or 225 mm, whichever figure is greater.
- The thickness of the flange plates to be half the thickness of the upper flange or 10 mm, whichever figure is greater.
- The thickness of the division plate to be at least half the thickness of the packing plate, or in the case of a welded splice, up to half of the difference in overall size of the two stanchion shafts spliced.

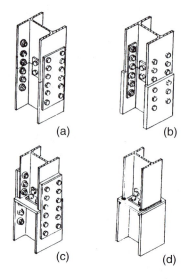

(a)　　　　(b)

(c)　　　　(d)

*Fig. 7.14.*

## 7.13. General notes on tension members

A member subjected to longitudinal tensile load is usually called a tie.

When a load is applied on the axis of centre of gravity of the cross-section, the tie is said to be *axially loaded* and the stress produced in the material is said to be a *direct tensile stress*. This stress is assumed uniform over the cross-sectional area of a straight member.

If there is no loss of the area of the member at connections, i.e. they are welded, the selection of the member is straightforward and the problem is reduced to selecting a member of sufficient area to ensure that the design strength is not exceeded.

This statement can be expressed in equation form as follows:

$$A = \frac{P_t}{p_y}$$

where:

$A$ = area of the required section

$P_t$ = factored load

$p_y$ = design strength of steel.

The area ($A$) in many cases will include allowances for holes at connections or eccentricities due to, say, only one leg of an angle being connected to a gusset. The effect of holes for fastenings is covered by §3.4 of the code, which gives rules for determining the effective area ($A_e$) at connections.

Failure of a tension member will occur either when the yield strength of the gross section has been reached, causing unacceptable extension, or when the ultimate strength has been achieved at the net cross area where holes have been drilled for fasteners. BS 5950 requires the designer to calculate the net area and then to modify this by a factor $K_e$ to calculate the effective area ($A_e$). The values of $K_e$ vary with the grade of steel and represent the difference between the ultimate and yield strengths of the material, modified to produce a suitable factor of safety. Thus:

$$K_e = 1.2 \text{ for grade S 275}$$
$$1.1 \text{ for grade S 355}$$
$$1.0 \text{ for grade S 460}$$
$$\text{For other grades } K_e = (U_s/1.2)/p_y$$

where:

$U_s$ is the specified minimum ultimate tensile strength.

In general, the stability of tension members is of minor concern. However, two cases must not be neglected and are specifically covered by the code. These are:

1 Members in roof trusses where wind loading could cause a reversal of stress putting the member into compression. This is covered by the wind loading code which requires uplift to be considered, and by limiting the slenderness ratio ($\lambda$) to 350 for such cases.

2 Members subjected to axial tension and moments. § 4.8.2.1 requires that such members should be capable of carrying the moments without the tension present. This is to ensure that members with low tension forces and high moments are checked adequately for any compression due to bending which may occur.

## 7.14. Types of tension members

The simplest structural steel tension members are round or square rods and flat rectangular bars.

Rods and bars are employed as tension members in bracing systems, such as diagonal bracing or anti-sag rods for purlins and internal members in small lattice trusses.

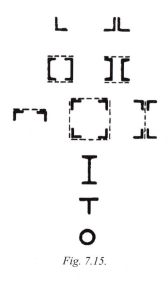

*Fig. 7.15.*

Angles, used singly or in pairs, are types of tension members widely used in light trusses. Also, members built up of plates and rolled sections are commonly used as tension members in heavier trusses. Fig. 7.15 shows some of the common configurations used as tension members.

Sections which extend the full length of the member are shown solid while intermittent sections, such as batten plates or lacing, are shown with a broken line.

## 7.15. Design of tension members

The design of tension members is covered by §4.6 and §4.8.2 of BS 5950. Design examples are given in the roof truss example in Chapter 9.

Members subjected to axial load and bending should be proportioned so that:

$$\frac{F_t}{P_t} + \frac{M_x}{M_{cx}} + \frac{M_y}{M_{cy}} \leq 1$$

where:

$F_t$ = axial load or tension at the critical location
$P_t$ = tension capacity = $p_y A_e$
$M_x$ = applied moment about the major axis at the critical location
$M_y$ = applied moment about the minor axis at the critical location
$M_{cx}$= moment capacity about the major axis in the absence of axial load
$M_{cy}$= moment capacity about the minor axis in the absence of axial load.

The approach is the same as for a compression member (see Fig. 7.8), except that the axial force is reversed.

The code also allows for plastic and compact sections, a more economical approach based on the reduced plastic moment capacity in the presence of axial load. This approach uses the methods adopted for plastic design of columns and requires that the following conditions be satisfied:

$$\left( \frac{M_x}{M_{rx}} \right)^{z_1} + \left( \frac{M_y}{M_{ry}} \right)^{z_2} \leq 1$$

where:

$M_{rx}$ is the reduced plastic moment capacity about the major axis in the presence of axial load obtained from published tables

$M_{ry}$ is the reduced plastic moment capacity about the minor axis in the presence of axial load obtained from published tables

$z_1$ is a constant, taken as:
2.0 for I- and H-sections with equal flanges and solid or hollow circular sections
5/3 for solid or hollow rectangular sections
1.0 for all other cases

$z_2$ is a constant, taken as:
1.0 for I- and H-sections
2.0 for solid or hollow circular sections
5/3 for solid or hollow rectangular sections
1.0 for all other cases.

It should be noted that $M_{rx}$ and $M_{ry}$ are calculated using the same formulae used for column calculations. The method has already been given in Section 5.4.4 of this book covering plastic analysis and design.

# 8.  Trussed structures

## 8.1. Definitions and types of frameworks

A truss is an arrangement of bars or members connected at joints. In many cases, such as roof trusses and lattice girders, it is assumed that, for design purposes, no significant moments are generated at the connections.

A frame which has all its members in one plane is called a plane frame, while a three-dimensional frame is called a space frame. The code puts the responsibility for checking that the whole frame is stable on the engineer; in particular he must ensure that there is adequate out-of-plane bracing in plane frames.

This chapter will refer to trussed frames where the principal forces on the members are either tensile or compressive. Trusses and lattice girders are generally considered as pin-jointed frames.

The term *pin-jointed* originated in the days of cast iron when the joints were, in fact, made by pins in holes cast into the ends of the members to be joined. Joints in structural steelwork are invariably bolted or welded, and although such joints will in fact transmit some moments from member to member, these moments are usually ignored in the determination of the forces acting in the frame. Thus when a triangulated frame is loaded at the joints, the internal forces developed in its members are axial tension or compression. If a local load is applied to a member between its end joints, however, bending moments and shear forces are induced in that member and the effects of these must be considered in the design of that member. The resulting joint forces are assumed as simple reactions applied to the frame at the joints.

A very simple frame is shown in Fig. 8.1. It consists of three individual members hinged at the ends to form a triangle. There is a vertical load $W$ applied at the apex C, producing reactions at the lower corners $R_a$ and $R_b$.

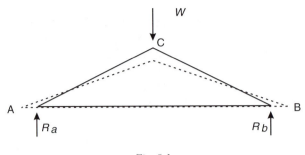

*Fig. 8.1.*

Under the action of the loading system, the frame tends to take the form in dotted lines, i.e. A and B move outwards putting member AB in tension, and C moves downwards putting members AC and BC in compression. AC and BC are termed *struts* and AB a *tie*.

The frame shown in Fig. 8.1 has just sufficient members to prevent it from being unstable. This sort of frame is known as a *statically determinate* or *isostatic* frame, and can be solved by statics alone. If there are $n$ members in a plane frame and $j$ joints, for a statically determinate plane frame $n = 2j - 3$.

If $n$ is less than $2j - 3$ then the frame is deficient and it will collapse under loading. This type of plane frame is known as a *mechanism*. The frame shown in Fig. 8.2(a) is an example of this type. To turn it into a statically determinate frame, another member must be added, as shown in Fig. 8.2(b).

If $n$ is more than $2j - 3$ the frame is redundant and cannot be analysed by statics alone. These frames are called *statically indeterminate* or *hyperstatic* frames. A redundant member is not necessarily a member without any load. For instance, member DB in Fig. 8.2(c) will be stressed and it will serve to create a stronger frame than the frame shown in Fig. 8.2(b).

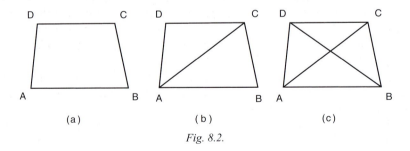

*Fig. 8.2.*

The simplest statically determinate truss has three pin joints and three members, i.e. the frame shown in Fig. 8.1. Each additional pin joint requires two additional members. So, a statically determinate frame can also be defined as a frame which is composed of the least number of members required to form a structure made up entirely of triangles. Fig. 8.3(a) shows another statically determinate frame. The deficient frame shown in Fig. 8.3(b), although it is stable under symmetrical loading, for unsymmetrical loading the frame would fail because distortion will occur. Therefore, mechanisms should be avoided because they are considered unstable.

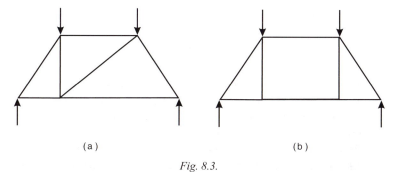

(a)        (b)

*Fig. 8.3.*

A roof truss is a type of plane frame consisting of sloping rafters which meet at the ridge, a main tie connecting the feet of the rafters and internal bracing members (see Fig. 8.4(b)).

The trusses support purlins, the latter being secondary members laid longitudinally along the rafter, which support the roof covering (see Fig. 8.4(a)). The internal bracing members of a truss should be so arranged that, under vertical loading, the longer members are in tension and the shorter members in compression. The arrangement of the internal bracing depends on its span. Rafters are normally divided into equal panel lengths and, ideally, the purlins should be supported at the node points, so that the rafters are subjected only to axial forces (Fig. 8.4(b)). However, in some cases purlins may have to be supported between node points; the rafters then have to be designed for bending and shear in addition to axial forces (Fig. 8.4(c)). (For the sake of clarity bracing has been omitted. The lateral support for a roof truss is shown in Fig. 8.22).

Some typical trusses and the spans for which they are suitable are shown in Fig. 8.5. Members with compressive forces under uniform vertical loading are shown with heavy lines.

The main ties in trusses of more than 15 metre span are usually cambered to counteract deflection and the illusory sagging effect, which is sometimes apparent in long-span members (Fig. 8.5d).

Long-span construction frequently employs lattice girders. These are plane frames with parallel chords or booms and internal web-bracing members.

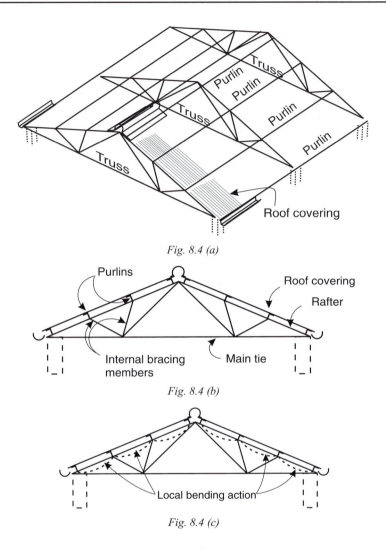

Fig. 8.4 (a)

Fig. 8.4 (b)

Fig. 8.4 (c)

Two main types of lattice girders are:

- the Warren type (Fig. 8.7(a))
- the N-type or Pratt type (Fig. 8.7(b))

The lattice girders of most steel bridges are either of these two types. When the load on a bridge is carried by the girders at the joints of the lower chord, the bridge is called a *through bridge* (Fig. 8.8(a)), and when carried at the joints of the upper chord it is called a *deck-type bridge* (Fig. 8.8(b)). Another lattice girder type, especially suitable for timber construction and used widely in the past in America, is the Howe girder (Fig. 8.9).

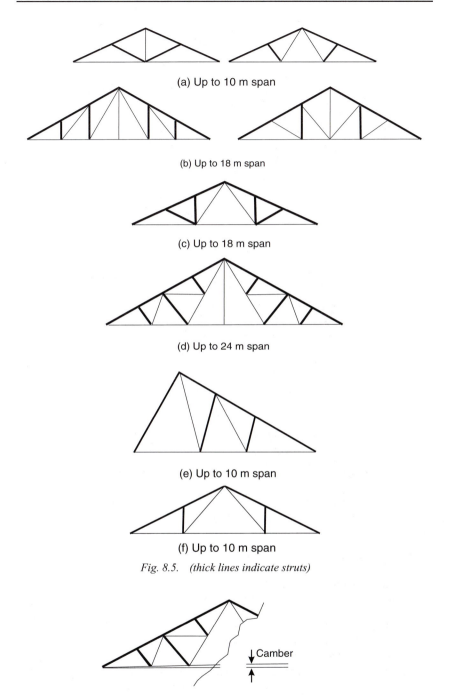

(a) Up to 10 m span

(b) Up to 18 m span

(c) Up to 18 m span

(d) Up to 24 m span

(e) Up to 10 m span

(f) Up to 10 m span

*Fig. 8.5.   (thick lines indicate struts)*

↓Camber

*Fig. 8.6.*

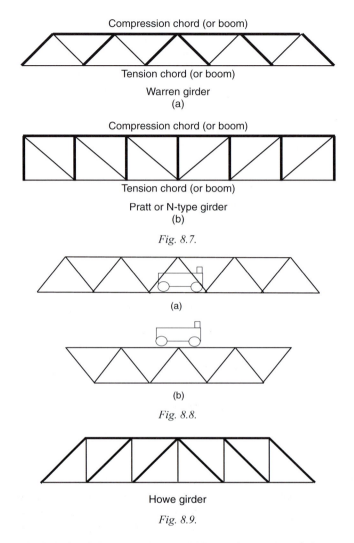

Compression chord (or boom)

Tension chord (or boom)

Warren girder
(a)

Compression chord (or boom)

Tension chord (or boom)

Pratt or N-type girder
(b)

*Fig. 8.7.*

(a)

(b)

*Fig. 8.8.*

Howe girder

*Fig. 8.9.*

A Vierendeel girder (Fig. 8.10) is one with no diagonal members, the only internal members being vertical. Since *n* is less than $2j - 3$, the joints are made rigid to achieve stability and high moments are present in the members.

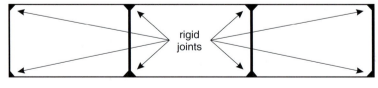

rigid
joints

Vierendeel girder

*Fig. 8.10.*

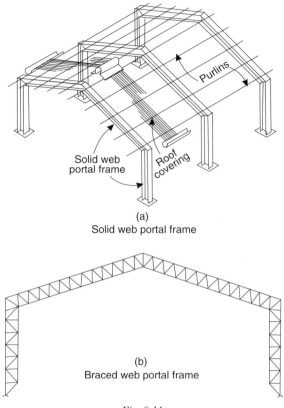

(a)
Solid web portal frame

(b)
Braced web portal frame

*Fig. 8.11.*

In industrial buildings, when a clear working space from floor to rafter level is required, a pitched portal frame is used (Fig. 8.11(a)). This consists of stanchions and roof beams connected rigidly to form a continuous plane frame. The portal frame can be of solid or open web construction (Fig. 8.11(b)). Chapter 10 will deal with portal frame design.

## 8.2. Methods of analysis of plane frames

Three methods of analysis are commonly used:

1. Graphical method.
2. Analytical methods by hand calculations. Method of sections and method of resolution at joints.
3. The use of a digital computer program. Most of these programs calculate the deflections in the frame as well as the forces on the members.

The simplified methods normally employed are based on the following assumptions:

- Loads are applied to the frame at the joints.
- All joints are pin-jointed and the members joined can freely rotate so that no moments are caused.

The second assumption is rarely true since the joints are bolted or welded; however, any errors caused by this assumption will not normally make the structure unsafe. If a computer is used for the analysis then the engineer can take advantage of its power to determine the secondary moments and shears as well as the axial forces.

### 8.2.1. Graphical method

In the graphical method, the forces in the members are determined by drawing a series of force polygons, one for each joint. However, it was found convenient to combine all these polygons into one figure called the *force diagram* or *Maxwell diagram* after Clerk Maxwell, Professor of Physics at King's College, London, who first proposed this method in 1864.

At any joint, the forces in the members and the external forces form a concurrent coplanar force system, which to be in equilibrium must produce a closed force polygon. Since the directions of all forces acting on a joint are known, by closing the force polygon for the joint, the magnitudes of two unknown forces in the members are determined.

Therefore, it is possible to determine all the forces in the members of a simple plane frame by starting at a joint where there are only two unknown forces and then considering each of the other joints in turn, always working with a joint where there are not more than two unknowns.

In applying the graphical method, the external and internal forces may be identified by using Bow's notation, named after the engineer RH Bow who first introduced it around 1870. To apply this notation, each space between external forces, either reactions or loads, is given a capital letter, usually working in a clockwise direction around the frame. Numbers usually denotes the spaces inside the frame.

The graphical method is best illustrated by example and the frame to be analysed is shown in Fig. 8.12.

Step 1    Label the frame using Bow's notation, and calculate the reactions.

Step 2    Draw the external factored loads and reactions to a convenient scale.

Step 3    Draw the force diagram, starting at any joint with no more than two unknowns.

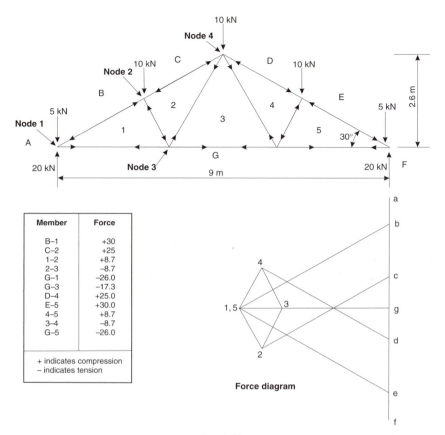

| Member | Force |
|--------|-------|
| B–1 | +30 |
| C–2 | +25 |
| 1–2 | +8.7 |
| 2–3 | –8.7 |
| G–1 | –26.0 |
| G–3 | –17.3 |
| D–4 | +25.0 |
| E–5 | +30.0 |
| 4–5 | +8.7 |
| 3–4 | –8.7 |
| G–5 | –26.0 |

+ indicates compression
– indicates tension

*Fig. 8.12.*

Starting on the left hand side, point 1 on the force diagram is found by drawing b–1 parallel to B–1 and g–1 parallel to G–1.

Point 1 lies on the intersection of these lines.

Point 2 can be found by drawing c–2 parallel to C–2 and 1–2 parallel to 1–2. The intersection of these two lines will give point 2.

Point 3 can be found by drawing 2–3 on the force diagram parallel to 2–3 of the frame diagram, and g–3 parallel to G–3.

Points 4 and 5 are found in a similar manner, though in this example, since the frame is symmetrical and symmetrically loaded, only half of the force diagram need have been drawn.

The direction of action of the forces can now be found.

Taking node 1 and moving clockwise, force AB is known to be downwards; the next force is B–1, and b–1 on the force diagram is going to the left and downwards. Then force 1–G acts from left to right, since 1–g on the force diagram acts from left to right.

This procedure is repeated at the other node points and all the directions of the forces obtained. If the internal forces in a member act away from its end, then the external forces, which must be equal and opposite to the internal forces, produce tension. The member is thus a tie, as, for example, member G–1. The reverse is true for the compression member or strut, as, for example, member B–1.

The final step, step 4, is to scale the amounts of all the forces from the force diagram, and to tabulate these with the appropriate sign convention indicating what type of forces they are (see Figure. 8.12).

### 8.2.2. Analytical methods

#### 8.2.2.1. Free body diagrams

The truss is an extremely suitable type of structure for use in the explanation of the free body diagram concept.

The free body concept is based on a very sensible notion; when a structure as a whole is a body in equilibrium, any part of it must also be a body in equilibrium. A portion of a structure may be imagined to be cut free from the whole, and this portion will be in equilibrium under the action of any applied loads acting on it and of the internal forces in the members that are cut.

The diagram which has such a portion of a structure on it is known as a *free body diagram.*

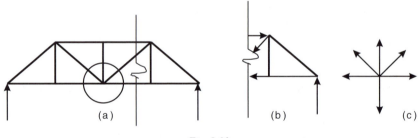

(a)      (b)      (c)

*Fig. 8.13.*

Two typical free body diagrams may be drawn for a truss, shown in Fig. 8.13(a).

One (Fig. 8.13(b)) results from a cut across the structure. The other (Fig. 8.13(c)) is obtained from a cut around a joint.

The first type of diagram is used in the method of analysis known as the method of sections, and the other is that known as the method of resolution at joints.

### 8.2.2.2. Method of sections

In this method, first proposed by A Ritter in 1862, a fictitious section is made along a convenient line, cutting not more than three non-concurrent members in which the forces are unknown; then the internal forces are replaced by equivalent external forces. Finally, moments are taken about some convenient point.

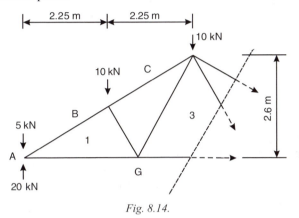

*Fig. 8.14.*

The frame on one side of the section is kept in equilibrium by the external forces, including the 'equivalent external forces' replacing the frame on the other side of the section. In the example in Fig. 8.14, if moments are taken about the node at the ridge then the only unknown force is that in the tie, G–3. This can then be determined by taking the forces and their lever arm distance from the node to give the value of the force in the tie.

*Example 8.2.2.2.1. Find force G–3 of the previous frame using the method of sections.*

Draw a section as shown in Fig. 8.14 and take moments about the apex.

$$20 \times 4.5 = 5 \times 4.5 + 10 \times 2.25 + G\text{–}3 \times 2.6$$

$$90 = 22.5 + 22.5 + G\text{–}3 \times 2.6$$

$$G\text{–}3 = \frac{90 - 45}{2.6} = 17.3 \text{ kN}$$

### 8.2.2.3. Method of resolution at joints

DJ Jourawski proposed this method in 1850. Here the equilibrium of each joint of the framework is considered, resolving all forces vertically and horizontally. Thus a number of equations are produced, some of which are solved directly and some simultaneously.

For example, consider node 1 in Fig. 8.14:

$$\updownarrow 20 - 5 = (\text{B}-1) \sin 30°$$

$$(\text{B}-1) = \frac{15}{0.5} = 30 \, \text{kN}$$

$$\leftrightarrow \text{G}-1 = \text{B}-1 \cos 30° = 30 \times 0.866 = 26.0 \, \text{kN}$$

This method can be very tedious and it lost popularity after the graphical method became established. However, this method lends itself best to mechanised evaluation.

### 8.2.3. Comments on the methods of analysis

In general, graphical methods are most useful where the members of the structure are inclined at many different angles and lengths of members vary, and where loads are applied in various directions. Also, when the forces in all the members have to be found, the force diagram is usually the most convenient method.

Analytical methods, as compared with graphical ones, are probably quicker when the shape of the framework and the application of the loading is simple and symmetrical. In particular, the method of sections is of greater value with lattice girders, i.e. parallel-chord trusses, where the locations of the largest internal forces are generally obvious.

Analytical methods are usually quicker if the forces in all members are not required.

## 8.3. Design of roof trusses

### 8.3.1. Notes on spacing and roof slopes of trusses

The usual economical spacing of roof trusses ranges between 4 m and 7.5 m, with the lower limit for short truss spans and the higher limit for spans of about 25 m and over.

Roof slopes vary with locality, imposed load, heating requirements and type of roof covering. There is now more demand for flat or nearly flat roof systems using parallel boom-type trusses. In areas where there is a high degree of exposure or where there is heavy rainfall or snowfall, roof trusses should have steeper pitches than in other cases. The traditional angle of a pitched roof is normally about 22.5°. Usually, the manufacturers of roof coverings recommend suitable slopes for their products. The vertical height of trusses varies usually from one quarter to one fifth of the span, giving a slope varying between 26.5° and 21.5°. Roofs which are completely flat are not normally used as there must be some fall to drainage points to ensure the adequate disposal of rainwater and avoid the formation of pools of water on the roof covering.

## 8.3.2. Design of purlins

Empirical rules for the design of purlins are given in §4.12.4.

### General rules for empirical design

- The members should be of steel to a minimum of grade S 275 to BS EN 10025.
- Unfactored loads should be considered for empirical design, i.e. effectively $\gamma_f = 1.0$.
- The span of the members should not exceed 6.5 metres, centre-to-centre of main supports.
- Where the members generally span only one bay, each member should be connected by at least two fasteners at each end.
- Where the members are generally continuous over two or more bays, with staggered joints in adjacent lines of members, at least one end of any single bay members should be connected by not less than two fasteners.

### Specific rules for the empirical design of purlins:

- *Slope.* The slope of the roof should not exceed 30° from the horizontal.
- *Loading.*
  (1) The loading on the purlin should be substantially uniformly distributed. Not more than 10 per cent of the total roof load on the member should be due to other types of load.
  (2) Imposed load should be determined as recommended in §2.2 of BS 5950, but should not be taken as less than 0.60 kN/m$^2$.
- *Elastic modulus.* The elastic modulus, $Z$, of a purlin about its axis parallel to the plane of the cladding should be not less than the values given in BS 5950 Table 27, Fig. 8.15.
- *Dimensions.* The dimension $D$ of the member perpendicular to the plane of the cladding, and, where applicable, the dimension $B$ parallel to the plane of the cladding, should be not less than the values given in BS 5950 Table 27, Fig. 8.15.

It must be noted that the only place in the code where there is any mention of carrying out design using unfactored loads is the section on purlins and side rails. The reason for this is that the rules given are empirical and based on experience from earlier versions of the code.

*BS 5950 Table 27. Empirical values for purlins*

| Purlin section | $Z_p$ (minimum) cm$^3$ | $Z_q$ (cm$^3$) | | D (mm) | B (mm) |
|---|---|---|---|---|---|
| | | Wind load based on BS 6399: Part 2 | Wind load based on CP3: ChV: Part 2 | | |
| Angle | $\dfrac{W_p L}{1800}$ | $\dfrac{W_q L}{2250}$ | $\dfrac{W_q L}{1800}$ | L/45 | L/60 |
| CHS | $\dfrac{W_p L}{2000}$ | $\dfrac{W_q L}{2500}$ | $\dfrac{W_q L}{2000}$ | L/65 | – |
| RHS | $\dfrac{W_p L}{1800}$ | $\dfrac{W_q L}{2250}$ | $\dfrac{W_q L}{1800}$ | L/70 | L/150 |

Note 1: $W_p$ and $W_q$ are the unfactored loads (kN) on one span of the purlin, acting perpendicularly to the plane of the cladding, due to (dead plus imposed) and (wind minus dead) loading, respectively.

Note 2: $L$ is the span of the purlin in mm, centre-to-centre of the main vertical supports. However, if properly supported anti-sag rods are used, $L$ may be taken as the anti-sag rod spacing in the determination of $B$ only.

*Fig. 8.15.*

*Example 8.3.2.1. A simplified example of a roof truss is taken as shown in Fig. 8.12. Purlins are assumed to be positioned at node points in order that no bending moment is induced in the rafters. The roof trusses are spaced at 4 metre centres and the loading is assumed to be 0.75 kN/m$^2$ imposed and 0.21 kN/m$^2$ dead load. Choose suitable purlin sections.*

## SOLUTION

Total load on the purlin $= 0.96 \times (4 \times 2.6) = 10.0$ kN.
From BS 5950 Table 27:

$$\text{Minimum depth required} = \frac{L}{45} = \frac{4000}{45} = 88.89 \text{ mm}$$

$$\text{Minimum width required} = \frac{L}{60} = \frac{4000}{60} = 66.67 \text{ mm}$$

$$\text{Minimum } Z \text{ required} = \frac{W_p L}{1800} = \frac{10 \times 4 \times 1000}{1800} = 22.22 \text{ cm}^3$$

A 125 × 75 × 8 angle has a Z of 29.6 cm$^3$ and is the lightest section to satisfy all the requirements of BS 5950 Table 27. A slightly heavier and more compact section, which will also satisfy the requirements, provided that the wind loading to BS 6399 does not exceed 10 kN/m$^2$, is a 100 × 75 × 10 angle (Z = 23.8 cm$^3$).

Fig. 8.16 shows details of the angle purlin arrangement.

As an alternative to the angle it is also possible to use a Rectangular Hollow Section (RHS). The limits in this case are different, allowing for the difference in behaviour of such sections. These limits in this case are:

$$\text{Minimum depth required} = \frac{L}{70} = \frac{4\,000}{70} = 57.14 \text{ mm}$$

$$\text{Minimum width required} = \frac{L}{150} = \frac{4\,000}{150} = 26.67 \text{ mm}$$

$$\text{Minimum } Z \text{ required} = \frac{W_p L}{1\,800} = 22.22 \text{ cm}^3$$

The lightest RHS which meets these requirements is a 100 × 50 × 3.2 RHS (Z = 23.5 cm$^3$). The mass per metre for this section is 7.18 kg as against 10.6 kg for the 125 × 75 × 8 angle.

In practical terms, the RHS would be a more stable section, although they are not used as frequently as the apparent savings would seem to justify.

Other forms of purlin, made from cold-rolled sections, are given in Appendix E.

## 8.4. Design of a typical ridge-type roof truss

### 8.4.1. Particulars of the scheme

- Size of building: 18 m span (centres of side stanchions), 40 m long (centres of gable stanchions)
- Covering: metal decking with thermal insulation. Assume that purlins are at 1.95 m centres (at node points of truss) and that the weight of the sheeting and purlins is 0.25 kN/m$^2$
- Spacing of trusses: 4 m
- Height of truss: one-fifth of span
- Material used: Grade S 275 steel

### 8.4.2. Design of purlins

The dead load, including the self-weight of the angle purlin, is 250 N/m$^2$ on slope.

The imposed load is 0.60 kN/m$^2$ or 600 N/m$^2$ on plan area. This load must be converted into a load on slope in order to be added to the dead load.

This is done by multiplying the figure of 600 N/m² by the cosine of the slope angle (0.930), giving a figure of 558 N/m², say 560 N/m².

Therefore, total load on slope = 250 + 560 = 810 N/m², unfactored.

Using the empirical rules:

$$\text{Minimum depth} = \frac{L}{45} = \frac{4\,000}{45} = 88.90\,\text{mm}$$

$$\text{Minimum width} = \frac{L}{60} = \frac{4\,000}{60} = 66.67\,\text{mm}$$

$$\text{Minimum } Z = \frac{W_p\,L}{1\,800} = \frac{810 \times 1.95 \times 4 \times 4\,000}{1\,800 \times 1\,000} = 14.04\,\text{cm}^3$$

A 100 × 65 × 7 mm angle has a Z of 16.6 cm³. The depth figure is satisfactory, but the width figure is slightly below what is required. The deficiency is so small as to be acceptable to most designers. However, if a designer feels that this is important, then he may choose a wider section.

This empirical method is allowed for roofs with slopes of less than 30°. If the roof has a steeper pitch than this, as say in a mansard roof, then the forces must be resolved in the direction of the two main axes of the purlin, and the purlin must be designed in accordance with §4.9 of BS 5950.

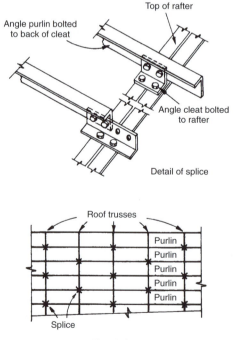

*Fig. 8.16.*

### 8.4.3. Determination of forces in roof truss members

A self-weight for the truss of 100 N/m² on slope is assumed. The self-weight of trusses for various spans may be obtained from Tables (Fig. 8.17 shows one such table).

*Weights of roof trusses*

| Span m | Number of panels in each rafter | Truss centres m | Weight kN |
|--------|----------------------------------|------------------|-----------|
| 7.5 | 2 | 3.00 | 2.00 |
| 9.0 | 3 | 3.75 | 2.75 |
| 10.5 | 3 | 3.75 | 3.33 |
| 12.0 | 4 | 3.75 | 4.33 |
| 13.5 | 4 | 3.75 | 5.33 |
| 15.0 | 4 | 3.75 | 6.33 |
| 16.5 | 5 | 4.50 | 7.33 |
| 18.0 | 5 | 4.50 | 8.66 |
| 19.0 | 6 | 4.50 | 9.66 |
| 21.0 | 6 | 4.50 | 11.00 |
| 22.5 | 6 | 4.50 | 13.66 |
| 24.0 | 6 | 4.50 | 16.50 |

Figures for the approximate weights given above are for design purposes only and should not be used for estimating costs.

The weight of steel trusses usually varies between 80 N/m² and 140 N/m².

*Fig. 8.17.*

Total dead load = $(250 + 100) \times 1.4/10^3 = 0.490$ kN/m²

Total imposed load = $560 \times 1.6/10^3 = 0.896$ kN/m²

Total DL + IL = 1.386 kN/m²

Total DL + IL on a rafter = $10 \times 4 \times 1.386 = 55.440$ kN

Load per node = $\dfrac{55.440}{5} = 11.1$ kN

There are four intermediate points and two ends, where the load is fifty per cent of that on the intermediate points, making the equivalent of ten points in all.

The frame and the force diagram are shown in Fig. 8.18.

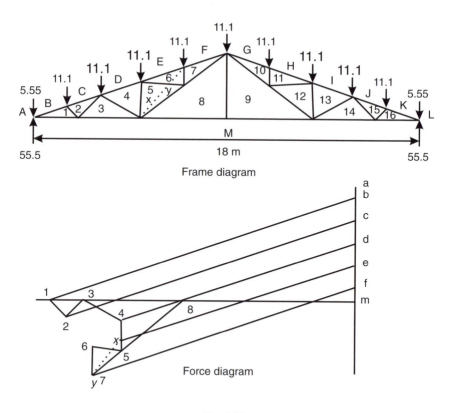

*Fig. 8.18.*

Note: In drawing the force diagram, a temporary modification must be made to the truss framing. Point 5 cannot be located because there are three unknowns (points 7 and 8 are not yet known). There are two ways to proceed, either by calculation or by replacement of members. Members 5–6 and 6–7 are replaced temporarily by an imaginary member x–y. (This substitution is justifiable because the force in member F–7 remains the same.) Then the drawing of the force diagram proceeds in the normal way. Points 7 and 8 are located, leading in turn to the location of point 5. A table of forces in the roof truss members is shown in Fig. 8.19. Alternatively, a computer program may be employed.

| Member | Force | Member | Force |
|--------|-------|--------|-------|
| B–1 | 134.5 | 4–5 | 16.6 |
| C–2 | 130.2 | 5–6 | –9.4 |
| D–4 | 104.6 | 6–7 | 11.1 |
| E–6 | 114.6 | 5–8 | –39.2 |
| F–7 | 114.6 | 7–8 | –52.3 |
| 1–2 | 10.3 | M–1 | –124.9 |
| 2–3 | –13.7 | M–3 | –111.0 |
| 3–4 | 17.8 | M–8 | –69.4 |

Note:  + indicates compression forces
       – indicates tension forces

*Fig. 8.19.*

In the normal design in practice there are three basic loads:

- Dead Load
- Imposed Load
- Wind Load

There are four combinations of the above loads:

- Dead load alone
- Dead load plus imposed load
- Dead load plus imposed load plus wind load
- Dead load plus wind load

In the worked example, combination 2 (dead load plus imposed load) was assumed to be the design criterion, because in most 'normal' roof truss designs this is the case. However, in practice all the above combinations must be considered, particularly if the wind load is high. If the force due to the wind is greater than that due to the dead load, then combination 4 (dead load plus wind load) above becomes important, because stress reversal occurs, i.e. a member that was a tie under a dead load condition now becomes a strut and vice versa. Combination 4 should always be checked when a lightweight roof cladding is used. It should also be noted that any services load applied to the truss should not be taken into account when considering uplift as there is no guarantee that it will be present during high wind (this is a requirement of BS 6399: Part 1).

### 8.4.4. Design of rafter

The purlins have been spaced in this example to carry metal deck, which has been assumed to be capable of spanning a distance of up to 2 m. This means that the purlins will be fixed above each of the node points. Had this not been so, the rafter would have to be designed to carry both axial load and the moments generated in carrying the load to the node points. The design of such members is covered in §4.8.

The effective length in the plane of the rafters needs careful consideration; if the internal members are large and stiff, compared to the chord members, and there are substantial gussets to hold the connections in place then an adjusted effective length may be used. BS 5950 now specifies this in §4.7.10.3.

In this example, the maximum force in the rafters occurs in member B−1 and it is a compressive force of 134.5 kN. The maximum length of the member between restraints is 1.95 metres (1 950 mm).

Assume that the member will be an 80 × 60 × 6 double angle strut with the short legs connected to the gusset. Having the long legs outstanding will help the erection, as this will provide more lateral stiffness to the truss; it will also help with the lateral stiffness of the truss when carrying loading. (However, long legs connected to gussets are used in many cases.)

Assuming that the purlins can hold the truss in place laterally but will provide no moment connection then the effective length in the Y–Y direction will be equal to the purlin spacing, which in this case is the length of the member. About the X–X axis, however, §4.7.10.3 and Table 25 require the following check:

$$\lambda_x = 0.85 \frac{L_x}{r_x} \text{ but not less than } 0.7\frac{L_x}{r_x} + 30$$

In this case $\lambda_x = 0.85 \times 195/2.52 = 66$

but greater than $0.7 \times 195/2.52 + 30 = 84$

The critical ratio is, therefore, 84.

For failure about the Y–Y axis, the slenderness must be corrected for the lack of continuity between the two members. This is carried out in the following equation:

$$\lambda = \left[ \left( \frac{L_y}{r_y} \right)^2 + \lambda_c^2 \right]^{0.5} \text{ but not less than } 1.4\lambda_c$$

Where $\lambda_c$ is the slenderness of the component about its weakest axis ($= L_v / r_v$).

$$\lambda_c = \frac{195}{(1.29 \times 4)} = 37.79$$

In this case, $r_y = 3.82$ cm, $r_v = 1.29$ cm.

If there are four interconnections between the two angles forming the strut then:

$$\lambda = \left[ \left( \frac{195}{3.82} \right)^2 + 37.79^2 \right]^{0.5} = 63.5$$

This is greater than $1.4 \times 37.79 \ (= 52.9)$

The critical axis in this case is X–X where the slenderness is 84.

the value of $p_c = 154$ N/mm$^2$ (from Table 24(c) of BS 5950)

Axial load capacity or compression resistance

$$= 154 \times \frac{16.20}{10} = 249 \text{ kN}$$

The compression resistance is much greater than the axial force and consideration should be given to reducing the size of the section, unless there is a possibility that the purlins will be moved, in which case it would be prudent to leave the heavier section.

It should be noted that there is a requirement that there should be at least two intermediate connectors; in this case it will be necessary to provide three to meet the design criteria.

### 8.4.5. Design of the other struts

All the other struts are single discontinuous angle struts connected to gussets by not less than two bolts in line. The effective slenderness for these members is taken from Table 25 of BS 5950. For these single angles the slenderness should be taken as the highest value of:

(a) $0.85 \, L_v / r_v$ but greater than $0.7 L_v / r_v + 15$
(b) $L_a / r_a$ but greater than $0.7 L_a / r_a + 30$
(c) $0.85 \, L_b / r_b$ but greater than $0.7 L_b / r_b + 30$

*Members 3–4 and 4–5:*

Try a 65 × 50 × 6 mm angle with the long leg attached to the gusset or member. (The axes of the angles are shown in Figure 7.5.)

The least radius of gyration is 1.06 cm.

The radius of gyration about the A–A axis is 1.46 cm.

$$\lambda_v = 0.85 \times 2.16 \times 100/1.06 = 173 \text{ or } (0.7 \times 2.16 \times 100/1.06) + 15 = 158$$

$$\lambda_a = 2.16 \times 100/1.46 = 148 \text{ or } (0.7 \times 2.16 \times 100/1.46) + 30 = 134$$

$$\lambda_b = 0.85 \times 2.16 \times 100/2.03 = 90 \text{ or } (0.7 \times 2.16 \times 100/2.03) + 30 = 104$$

Failure will therefore occur about the V–V axis with a slenderness of 173.

From BS 5950 Table 24(c), $p_c = 54$ N/mm$^2$.
The capacity of the section $= 54 \times 658/10^3 = 35.5$ kN
This is greater than the force on the member $= 17.5$ kN

## 8.4.6. Design of ties

The main tie member on this truss is M–1 (in Fig. 8.18) at the support (it is worth drawing the reader's attention to the fact that the maximum forces in ordinary pitched trusses occur at the end members and not at the mid-span). (This applies in this truss, as can be seen from the table of member forces.)

For this member, try an 80 × 60 × 6 mm angle with the long leg attached to the gusset.

In general, ties are designed to §4.6 but in order to save designer's time, angle, channel and T-section ties are designed to §4.6.3.1. This gives rules to cover the eccentricities which occur without the necessity of full calculations.

The tension capacity of an angle tie is taken as:

For bolted connections: $P_t = p_y (A_e - 0.5a_2)$

For welded connections: $P_t = p_y (A_g - 0.3a_2)$

where:

$P_t$ is the axial tension capacity
$p_y$ is the design strength
$A_e$ is the effective area of the section taken from §3.4.3.
$A_g$ is the gross area of the section
$a_2$ is $A_g - a_1$
$a_1$ is the gross area of the connected element (width $x$ thickness)

The effective area of the angle is:

$$a_e = K_e a_n$$

where:

$K_e$ is a constant from §3.4.3 for grade S 275 steel $= 1.2$

$a_n$ is the net area of the element of the cross-section,

i.e. the gross area – the area of the holes in the section

The gross area of the connected leg is $80 \times 6 = 480 \text{ mm}^2$

Assuming that the connection is made with 20 mm diameter bolts then the area of the bolt holes will be:

$$22 \times 6 = 132 \text{ mm}^2$$

Note: the holes are drilled 2 mm larger than the bolt diameter to allow for a clearance during erection.

The net area $(a_n) = 480 - 132 = 348 \text{ mm}^2$

$A_e = 1.2 \times 348 = 418 \text{ mm}^2$ or $480 \text{ mm}^2$

The smaller value is used giving an effective area of $418 \text{ mm}^2$.
The effective area of the whole section is $418 + (54 \times 6) = 742 \text{ mm}^2$.
The tension capacity is $275(742 - 0.5 \times 54 \times 6)/10^3 = 159.5 \text{ kN}$
This section is adequate to carry the force.

### 8.4.7. Minimum sections recommended

Some sections found adequate in the Volume 1 tables referred to earlier may be too small if practical considerations are taken into account.

One such consideration, i.e. that the minimum leg of angle be suitable for connection purposes, has already been mentioned. Another consideration is that the frames be sufficiently robust to resist damage during loading, transport, off-loading and erection, assuming that the trusses are prefabricated in halves prior to despatch. The centre tie and a sag tie are usually sent to the site loose, but the former is particularly vulnerable to accidental distortion if it is not made stiff enough.

Another consideration is that members be sufficiently stiff not to deflect excessively under the loads of, say, light fittings, conduits, etc. which may be attached to the roof construction, although such loads are usually small.

To take account of these considerations minimum sections are recommended. These are as follows:

- For main struts, centre tie and main inclined ties or slings, a $65 \times 50 \times 6$ mm angle.
- For main ties, a $80 \times 60 \times 6$ mm angle.
- For all other members, a $50 \times 50 \times 6$ mm angle.

### 8.4.8. Typical details of roof truss connections

Typical details of bolted roof truss connections are shown in Fig. 8.20.

In drawing bolted connections, the gauge lines, i.e. the lines passing through the middle of the holes of the various members forming a joint meet in the manner indicated in Fig. 8.20(a).

Typical details of welded roof truss connections are shown in Fig. 8.20.

In drawing welded connections, the lines passing through the centroids of the angle members forming a joint meet in the manner indicated in Fig. 8.21(a).

Note: In some countries in Europe, bolted connections follow the same practice as welded connections, i.e. the lines pass through the centroids of the sections instead of the gauge lines.

A complete structure is shown in Fig. 8.22.

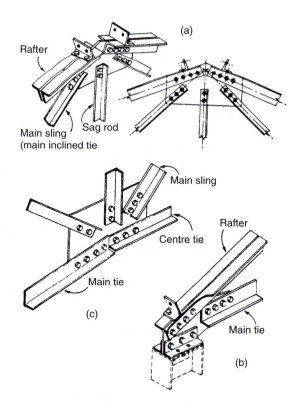

*Fig. 8.20.*

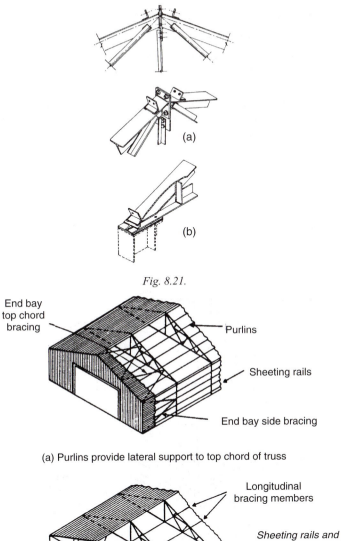

*Fig. 8.21.*

End bay top chord bracing

Purlins

Sheeting rails

End bay side bracing

(a) Purlins provide lateral support to top chord of truss

Longitudinal bracing members

*Sheeting rails and purlins not shown*

Lower chord bracing

Side bracing

(b) Lower chord bracing system provides lateral support to bottom chord of truss

*Fig. 8.22.*

# 9. Connections

## 9.1. General notes

Structural steelwork is assembled nowadays by bolting or welding. Riveting is rarely used today, although it was the oldest form of connecting steel structures. The behaviour of connections is a complex problem. Loads may be distributed unevenly through the joint due to the inexact fit of the parts joined. Sections may warp at the joints and plane sections will no longer remain plane. Most connections are highly indeterminate, with the distribution of the stress depending on the deformation of the fasteners and the parent material. Local restraints may also prevent the deformation necessary for simple stress distribution. For these reasons, a rigorous theoretical approach to the design of connections is always difficult. Therefore, the design of connections is approximate and most of the design methods are based on simple formulae derived analytically. The use of these formulae is justified by the consideration of the ultimate strength and test results.

## 9.2. Bolted connections

### 9.2.1. General notes

A bolt may be considered as a simple pin inserted in holes drilled in two or more steel plates or sections to prevent relative movement (see Fig. 9.1).

A bolt may sometimes strengthen the joint by pressing the two plates together but this strength cannot always be easily determined. The strength is therefore calculated on the assumption that only the shank of the bolt is contributing to the strength, unless the bolt is tightened to a predetermined torque (such as high strength friction bolts).

If the loads are large enough then the bolt may fail by shearing, as shown in Fig. 9.2. The area resisting this failure is the circular area of the bolt shank, or the tensile stress area if the threads are in the shear plane.

The capacity is given as the shear area of the bolt multiplied by the bolt strength in shear.

A bolt in a joint such as that shown in Fig. 9.3(a) has to shear across two planes in order to fail (Fig. 9.3(b)). This type of failure is known as double shear.

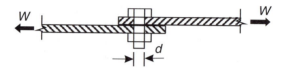

*Fig. 9.1.*

*Fig. 9.2.*

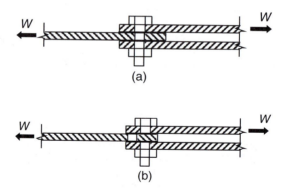

(a)

(b)

*Fig. 9.3*

The load required to break the bolt in double shear is twice that required to break the bolt in single shear. Thus using the circular area of the shank as before, the capacity in double shear is equal to the shear area × 2 × strength in single shear.

The shear type of failure assumes fairly thick plates capable of shearing the bolt. However, when a relatively large diameter bolt, say 24 mm diameter, connects two thin steel plates, say 4 mm, failure will take place when the steel plates are torn by the bolt. This type of failure is known as bearing or tearing.

The area of contact of the bolt with the plate on one side is actually semi-cylindrical (see Fig. 9.4), but since the variation of stress around the perimeter of the hole is indeterminate, the strength of the bolt in bearing is taken as the thickness of the plate multiplied by the diameter of the bolt multiplied by the bearing strength. Where the thicknesses of the plates are not equal, the thinner plate will tear first, so the thickness of the thinner plate is taken in the above product (see Fig. 9.4).

In the case of cover plates on both sides of a member, as shown in Fig. 9.5, the two 16 mm cover plates act together, giving a thickness of 32 mm; therefore the smaller thickness for the connection shown is 24 mm.

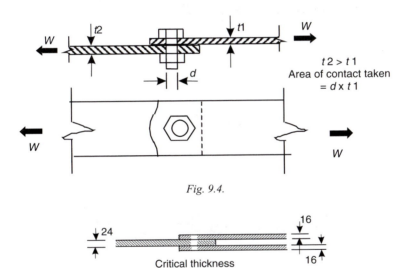

*Fig. 9.4.*

Critical thickness
smaller of either
24 mm or 2 × 16 = 32 mm

*Fig. 9.5.*

## 9.2.2. Design strengths

The design strengths are given in the following tables, taken from BS 5950. Tables 30 and 31 are given in Fig. 9.6 and Table 32 is given in Fig. 9.8.

BS 5950 Tables 30 and 31. Strength of bolts in clearance holes

| | Bolt grade Gr 4.6 $N/mm^2$ | Bolt grade Gr 8.8 $N/mm^2$ | Other grades of bolts $N/mm^2$ |
|---|---|---|---|
| Shear strength $p_s$ | 160 | 375 | $0.4U_b$ but not greater than 400 |
| Bearing strength $p_{bb}$ | 460 | 1000 | $0.7(U_b + Y_b)$ |
| Tension strength* $p_t$ | 240 | 560 | $0.7U_b$ but not greater than $Y_b$ |

\* These values assume that prying forces are included in the design of the connections. If not then the tension values should be reduced to 80 per cent of those in the table.
$Y_b$ is the specified minimum yield strength of the bolt.
$U_b$ is the specified minimum tensile strength of the bolt.

*Fig. 9.6*

The effects of prying action are illustrated in Fig. 9.7, where the plate in the connection is pulled away from the flange to which it is connected. The result is a compressive force at the edges of the plate which absorbs part of the tensile strength of the bolt. Previous versions of BS 5950 have just reduced the tension strength of the bolts to compensate for this, but the present version has given limits on this simple approach and required a detailed calculation in other cases. Unfortunately, no method for this has been given.

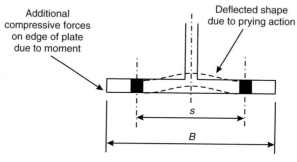

*Fig. 9.7.*

*BS 5950 Table 32. Bearing strength of connected parts for ordinary bolts in clearance holes, $p_{bs}$*

Steel to BS EN 10025 and BS EN 10113 N/mm²

| Grade 275 | Grade 355 | Grade 460 | Other grades |
|-----------|-----------|-----------|--------------|
| 460 | 550 | 670 | $0.67(U_s + Y_s)$ |

$Y_s$ is the specified minimum yield strength of the steel.
$U_s$ is the specified minimum tensile strength of the steel.

*Fig. 9.8.*

The strengths tabulated above are based on $A_s$, the shear area, for all bolts. Since threads can occur in the shear plane, $A_s$ is then taken as the tensile stress area, $A_t$, given in Fig. 9.9. For bolts where $A_t$ is not defined, it may be taken as the area at the bottom of the threads. Where it can be shown that the threads do not occur in the shear plane $A_s$ may be taken as the shank area, $A$.

Tensile stress areas

| Bolt diameter mm | Tensile stress area mm² $A_t$ |
|------------------|-------------------------------|
| (12) | 84.3 |
| 16 | 157 |
| 20 | 245 |
| (22) | 303 |
| 24 | 353 |
| (27) | 459 |
| 30 | 561 |

Note: bolts whose size is enclosed in brackets are not commonly used.

*Fig. 9.9.*

## 9.2.3. Bolt grades

With the introduction of ISO standards, the continental method of bolt grading has been introduced in British Standards. The strength of the bolt is given by two figures separated by a point. The first figure is 1/10th of the minimum ultimate strength in kgf/mm² and the second is 1/10th of the percentage ratio of the minimum yield stress to the minimum ultimate stress. Thus '4.6 grade' means that the minimum ultimate strength is 40 kgf/mm$^2$ and the yield strength is 60 per cent of this. It follows that the yield stress is obtained by multiplying the two figures together to give 24 kgf/mm$^2$.

### 9.2.4. Bolting

Black bolts are manufactured from rolled steel bars; they are known as black bolts because the original form of the bolts was black; however, it is not necessarily true that they are always black. The term 'black' is now applied to unfinished common or rough bolts which have not been finished to a close tolerance. In order to overcome the problems of tolerance in the bolt diameters and drilling, it is customary to drill holes greater in diameter than that of the bolt. The normal allowances are 2 mm for bolts up to 24 mm in diameter and 3 mm for larger bolts. Black bolts are used in situations where there is no requirement for slip resistance or where vibration is not a design requirement.

Close tolerance bolts are used very little today. They are made from rolled steel bars, which are greater in diameter than the required size of the bolt and subsequently turned down to the required diameter. It is normal practice to drill holes for these bolts to a tolerance of 0.15 mm. In order to ensure a fit, the holes are drilled either with the plates clamped together or using hardened steel templates clamped to the parts being drilled.

The capacity of each bolt is determined from the strength multiplied by the appropriate area as follows:

### (a) Shear capacity

The shear capacity, $P_S$, of a bolt should be taken as:

$$P_S = p_s A_s$$

where:

$p_s$ is the shear strength obtained from Table 30
$A_s$ is the shear area as defined earlier, i.e. $A_t$ or $A$

It should be noted that the threads may occur in the shear plane as mentioned above.

### (b) Bearing capacity

The bearing capacity, $P_{bb}$ of a bolt should be taken as:

$$P_{bb} = dt_p p_{bb}$$

where:

$d$ is the nominal diameter

$t_p$ is the thickness of the connected part, or, if the bolts are countersunk, the thickness of the part minus half the depth of countersinking

$p_{bb}$ is the bearing strength of the bolt obtained from Table 31

### (c) Tension capacity

The tension capacity, $P_t$, of a bolt (including countersunk bolts) should be taken as:

$$P_t = p_t A_t$$

where:

$p_t$ is the tension strength obtained from BS 5950 Table 34
$A_t$ is the tensile stress area as defined earlier

When bolts are subjected to both shear and tension then the following relationship should be satisfied:

$$\frac{F_s}{P_s} + \frac{F_t}{P_t} \leq 1.4$$

where:

$F_s$ is the applied shear
$F_t$ is applied tension
$P_s$ the shear capacity
$P_t$ is the tension capacity
In addition, $F_s \leq P_s$ and $F_t \leq P_t$

This interaction may be demonstrated graphically.

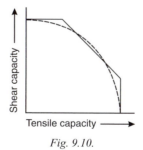

*Fig. 9.10.*

It will be found that other codes, i.e. BS 5400, give a more elaborate equation using an elliptical interaction. This is shown in Fig. 9.10 as a dotted line. The difference between the two approaches is very small, but the elliptical approach has the disadvantage that combined force calculations must be carried out at all values of shear and tension.

## 9.2.5. Bolt spacing and edge distances

### Minimum spacing

The spacing between centres of bolts should be not less than 2.5 times the nominal diameter of the bolt to ensure that they are fully effective.

### Maximum spacing in unstiffened plates.

The spacing between centres of two adjacent bolts in a line lying in the direction of stress should not exceed $14t$ where $t$ is the thickness of the thinner element. Where the members are exposed to corrosive influences, the maximum spacing of bolts in any direction should not exceed $16t$ or 200 mm, where $t$ is the thickness of the thinner outside plate.

### Minimum edge and end distances

The distance from the centre of a bolt hole to the edge or end of any part should be not less than the value given in BS 5950 Table 29 (Fig. 9.11).

The edge distance is the distance from the centre of a hole to the adjacent edge at right angles to the direction of stress. The end distance is the distance from the centre of a hole to the adjacent edge in the direction in which the bolt bears. The end distances should also be sufficient to provide adequate bearing capacity.

---

*BS 5950 Table 29 Minimum edge and end distances of bolts*

| Quality of cut | Edge and end distances |
|---|---|
| For a rolled, machine flame cut, sawn or planed edge or end | $1.25D$ |
| For a sheared or hand flame cut edge or end | $1.40D$ |

Note: $D$ is the diameter of a standard clearance hole.

*Fig. 9.11.*

### Maximum edge or end distances.

The maximum distance to the nearest line of bolts from an edge of any unstiffened part should not exceed $11t\varepsilon$. This rule does not apply to bolts interconnecting the components of back-to-back tension members.

Where the members are exposed to corrosive influences, the maximum edge distance should not exceed 40 mm $+ 4t$, where $t$ is the thickness of the thinnest part.

## 9.2.6. Design examples of bolted connections

*Example 9.2.6.1. Two plates of 12 mm thickness, grade S 275 steel, are connected together by 20 mm diameter bolts. Assuming that the edge and end distances are greater than 1.25D and 2D respectively, calculate the strength of one bolt in the joint. The bolt is an ISO standard bolt, grade 8.8, with the threads in the shear plane.*

### SOLUTION

Shear strength

$$p_s = 375 \text{ N/mm}^2$$

Bearing strength

$$p_{bb} = 1\,000 \text{ N/mm}^2$$

Bearing strength

$$p_{bs} = 460 \text{ N/mm}^2$$

See Fig. 9.6 for the bolt
See Fig. 9.7 for the connected parts

Tension strength

$$p_t = 560 \text{ N/mm}^2$$

Assume that the connection complies with the requirements for simple connections and that the tensile strength is reduced to
80 per cent = $0.8 \times 560 = 448 \text{ N/mm}^2$

### (a) Shear capacity, $P_S = p_s A_s$

$A_s$ is $A_t$ here because the threads are in the shear plane. $A_t$ for an M20 bolt is 245 mm$^2$ (Fig. 9.9).

$$\text{Shear capacity, } P_s = \frac{375 \times 245}{10^3} = 91.9 \text{ kN}$$

### (b) Bearing capacity, $P_{bb} = dt_p p_{bb}$

$p_{bb}$ is based on the lower strength of the bolt or the connected part; since in this example the edge and end distances are greater than the minimum required for strength, the capacity is based on the lower of the plate strength (460 N/mm$^2$, Fig. 9.8) or the bolt strength (1 000 N/mm$^2$, Fig. 9.6).

$$\therefore p_{bb} = \frac{20 \times 12 \times 460}{10^3} = 110.4 \text{ kN}$$

Comparing (a) and (b), one sees that the shear capacity is lower than the bearing value.

*(c) Tensile capacity, $P_t = p_t A_t$*

$$P_t = \frac{448 \times 240}{10^3} = 108 \, \text{kN}$$

*(d) Combined tension and shear*

As already explained the capacity of a bolt under combined tension and shear is determined by the simple interaction formula:

$$\frac{F_s}{P_s} + \frac{F_t}{P_t} \leq 1.4$$

The diagram for the M20 bolt, plotted from figures obtained is:

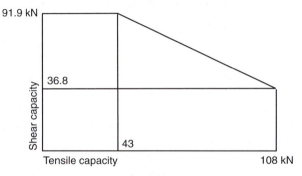

*Fig. 9.12.*

*Example 9.2.6.2. A tee-section is part of a beam-to-stanchion connection which is required to transfer 360 kN in tension and 120 kN in shear. Check if four grade 8.8 bolts of 20 mm diameter will be adequate, assuming the plates are 12 mm thick.*

*SOLUTION*

$$\frac{F_s}{P_s} + \frac{F_t}{P_t} \leq 1.4$$

$$F_t = \frac{360}{4} = 90 \, \text{kN}$$

$$F_s = \frac{120}{4} = 30 \, \text{kN}$$

From Example 9.2.6.1, in which the same diameter bolts and plate thicknesses are used.

$P_s = 91.9$ kN

$P_t = 108$ kN

Assuming that prying forces are not taken into account in the calculations.

Substituting into the equation:

$$\frac{30}{91.9} + \frac{90}{108}$$

$0.326 + 0.833 = 1.16 < 1.4$

∴ the bolts are satisfactory.

## 9.3. High strength friction grip (HSFG) bolts

The introduction of HSFG (pre-loaded) bolts has accelerated the obsolescence of riveting. HSFG bolts are normally used in standard clearance holes and give joints which, if properly assembled, are very stiff. In Britain, due to the requirements of the Health and Safety at Work Acts, the cost of installing and checking HSFG bolts has risen rapidly, causing their replacement with 8.8 bolts. The exception to this is in structures where the connections must not slip in order to prevent undue movement of the structure, or to reduce the chances of fatigue.

The strength of HSFG bolts results from tightening the bolts to a high tension, clamping the joined parts together to generate friction between the surfaces in contact. It is this friction which carries all the load through the joint.

In order to make the joints perform as intended by the engineer, it is essential to make sure that the contact or faying surfaces (the area between the plies compressed by the bolts to give a friction surface carrying the load) are properly prepared. Once they have been finished, a cover should be placed over them to ensure that they remain free from oil, paint, dirt, rust or other contamination. This is usually achieved by covering them with a waterproof cover, firmly fixed in place until just before assembly, when it is removed to leave the surface as intended by the designer. The type of finish has a major influence on the coefficient of friction, as shown in Table 35 of BS 5950.

HSFG bolts are made from high-tensile steel, which is tested for ductility to ensure that the required clamping force can be achieved. It is, therefore, necessary to use hardened steel washers beneath the heads and nuts. These prevent the heads and nuts being pulled into the surface of the connected parts, which are made of relatively much softer steel.

Finally, an advantage of HSFG bolts is that the method of tightening locks the nuts in place, generally preventing loosening of the bolts as a result of load reversal or vibration.

Summarising the advantages of HSFG bolts:

- Rigid joints with negligible slip between plates at working load.
- No shearing or bearing stresses in the bolts at working load.
- Good fatigue performance.
- Nuts are prevented from becoming loose.
- Higher tensile capacity.

### 9.3.1. Installation of HSFG bolts

Bolts may be tightened by three methods: torque control, part turn and direct tension indication.

In recent years, the first two methods have largely given way to direct tension indication and the majority of bolts now installed in Ireland and Britain employ one of the load indicating methods which register load directly.

The load indicator is a special washer with arched protrusions raised on one face (see Fig. 9.13). It is normally fitted under the standard bolt head with the protrusions facing the head, thus maintaining a gap between the

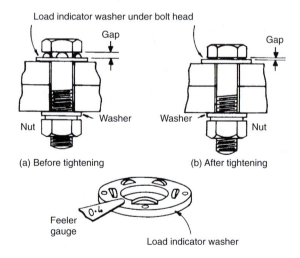

Fig. 9.13.

underside of the head and the load indicator face. On tightening the bolt, the gap reduces as the protrusions depress and when the specified gap, usually 0.40 mm, is obtained, the bolt tension will not be less than the required minimum (see Fig. 9.13). Gaps may be measured with a feeler gauge but, with a little practice, may be judged by eye with sufficient accuracy.

## 9.3.2. Design of HSFG bolts

The application of HSFG bolts should comply with the requirements of BS 4604, *The use of high strength friction grip bolts in structural engineering, metric series.*

For design purposes three types of connections are distinguished:

(a) Shear connections
(b) Tension connections
(c) Combined shear and tension connections

### (a) Shear connections

Shear connections may be considered in three ways:

- The connection is designed as a normal bearing connection in the same way as for black bolts given above. In this case the bolts are used as though they were normal bolts without any special tightening. They do not have the advantages of pre-tensioning.
- Those bolts which remain non-slip up to service load.
- Pre-loaded bolts designed to be non-slip up to full factored load.

For connections subjected to shear only in the plane of the friction faces, the slip resistance $P_{sL}$ at any bolt position has one of the following values:

$P_{sL} = 1.1 \ K_s \mu P_o$ for connections which are designed not to slip at service loads, or

$P_{sL} = 0.9 \ K_s \mu \ P_o$ for connections which are designed not to slip at factored loads

where:

$P_o$ is the minimum shank tension or proof load as specified in BS 4604
$\mu$ is the slip factor or coefficient of friction
$K_s = 1.0$ for pre-loaded bolts in clearance holes;
   $= 0.85$ for pre-loaded bolts in oversized and short slotted holes, and for fasteners in long slotted holes loaded perpendicularly to the slot;
   $= 0.7$ for pre-loaded bolts in long slotted holes loaded parallel to the slot

### (b) Tension connections

For bolts subjected only to external tension in the direction of the bolt axes, the tension capacity, $P_t$, is taken as either:

$\qquad$ 1.1$P_o$ in cases where slip is not permitted until service load

or

$\qquad$ 0.9$P_o$ where slip is not permitted until factored load

*Capacities of high strength friction grip bolts*

| Bolt diameter | Proof load of bolt | Tensile capacity | Slip value in single shear |
|---|---|---|---|
| *mm* | *kN* | *kN* | *kN* |
| (12) | 49.4 | 44.5 | 19.8 |
| 16 | 92.1 | 82.9 | 36.8 |
| 20 | 144 | 130 | 57.6 |
| (22) | 177 | 159 | 70.8 |
| 24 | 207 | 186 | 82.8 |
| (27) | 234 | 211 | 93.6 |
| 30 | 286 | 257 | 114.4 |

Note: These values apply to a single bolt on a slip plane assuming that the coefficient of friction is 0.40 for surfaces blast cleaned with shot or grit. If this value changes then the slip value must be changed accordingly.

*Fig. 9.14.*

### (c) Combined shear and tension connections

For these connections the following relationship should be satisfied:

$\dfrac{F_s}{P_{sL}} + \dfrac{F_{tot}}{1.1P_o} \le 1.0$, but $F_{tot} \le A_t p_t$ for cases designed to be non-slip in service

or

$\dfrac{F_s}{P_{sL}} + \dfrac{F_{tot}}{0.9P_o} \le 1.0$ for cases designed to be non-slip under factored loads

where:
$\qquad$ $F_s$ is the applied shear
$\qquad$ $F_{tot}$ is the total applied tension in the bolt

The equation may be plotted as shown in Fig. 9.15. This indicates that for normal HSFG bolts the behaviour is different from that of black bolts.

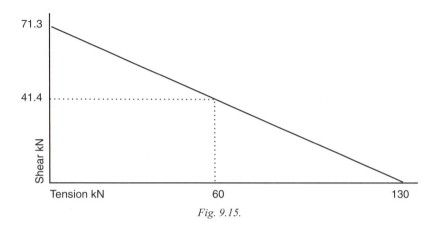

*Fig. 9.15.*

*Example 9.3.2.1. Find the capacity in single shear of a 20 mm diameter HSFG bolt assuming a value of $\mu = 0.45$. Find also the capacity if, in addition to shear, there is a direct tension of 60 kN acting on the bolt. (The minimum shank tension of the bolt is 144 kN, see Fig. 9.14.) It may be assumed that slip can occur at service load.*

SOLUTION

$$P_{sL} = 1.1\, K_s\, \mu\, P_o$$

$$P_{sL} = 1.1 \times 1 \times 0.45 \times 144 = 71.3 \text{ kN}$$

$$P_t = 0.9 P_o = 0.9 \times 144 = 129.6 \text{ kN, say } 130.0 \text{ kN}$$

$$F_t = 60 \text{ kN}$$

$$\frac{F_s}{P_{sL}} + \frac{F_{tot}}{1.1 P_o} \leq 1.0$$

$$\frac{F_s}{71.3} + \frac{60}{1.1 \times 130} = 1$$

$$\therefore F_s = 71.3 - 60 \times \frac{71.3}{\left(1.1 \times 130\right)} = 41.4$$

## 9.4. Block shear failure

As a result of some research work carried out in the USA, it was found that there are certain cases where failure in a connection is caused by a block of material within the bolted area breaking away from the remainder of the section. This has become known as *block shear failure*. Some typical cases of this are shown in Fig. 9.16, taken from §6.2.4.

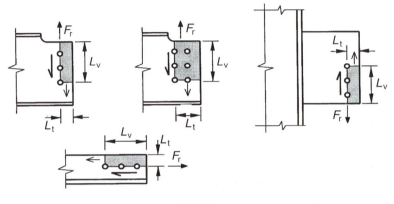

*Fig. 9.16.*

The check for this type of failure is carried out by using the following equation §6.2.4:

$$P_r = 0.6 p_y t \left[ L_v + K_e \left( L_t - k D_t \right) \right]$$

where:

$P_r$ is the block shear capacity
$p_y$ is the design strength of the web or plate
$t$ is the web or plate thickness
$L_v$ is the length of the shear face (see Fig. 9.16)
$K_e$ is the effective net area coefficient
$L_t$ is the length of the tension face (see Fig. 9.16)
$k$ is a coefficient, 0.5 for a single line of bolts and 2.5 for a double line
$D_t$ is the diameter of the hole, except when they are slotted

*Example 9.4.1. A 686 × 254 × 125 UB is connected to a column by web cleats with a single row of bolts. If the reaction is 350 kN and there are four 20mm diameter bolts through the web, as in Fig. 9.17, check if the section is adequate for block shear failure.*

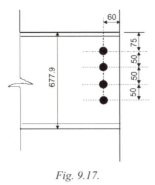

*Fig. 9.17.*

The values for this particular case are:

$p_y$ design strength of the web = 265 N/mm$^2$ (T = 16.5 mm)
$t$ is the web or plate thickness = 11.7 mm
$L_v$ is the length of the shear face = 225 mm
$K_e$ is the effective net area coefficient = 1.2
$L_t$ is the length of the tension face = 60 mm
$k$ is a coefficient, 0.5 for a single line of bolts
$D_t$ is the diameter of the hole = 22 mm

$$\text{Block shear capacity} = 0.6 \times 265 \times 11.7 \big[225 + 1.2(60 - 0.5 \times 22)\big] / 10^3$$
$$= 528 \text{ kN}$$

This is very much higher than the applied reaction, therefore, there will be no block shear failure in this case.

## 9.5. Welding

Welding is a process of connecting pieces of metal together by fusion, thus establishing a metallurgical bond between them. By this bonding, welding is distinguished from other connection methods which rely on friction or other mechanical means.

### 9.5.1. Arc-welding process

The most widely used process of welding for structural purposes is arc-welding.

Credit for the development of arc-welding is generally given to Sir Humphrey Davy, because of his discovery of the electric arc in the first part of the nineteenth century. However, in 1887, a Russian scientist, MV Bernardos, originated the use of an electric arc for melting metals.

The intense heat required is created by an electric arc, which is a sustained spark between the work to be welded and a metal filler wire called an electrode or welding rod. The electrode, held in a suitable holder, is brought close to the metal area to be welded, forming an arc between the tip of the electrode and the work. At the instant the arc is formed, a temperature of 3 500 °C is reached, causing melting at the tip of the electrode and the local regions of the parts to be connected.

Fusion of the filler wire causes the filler material to be transferred into the joint by the arc in any direction.

Directing and moving the electrode in the proper fashion will deposit the molten electrode metal in the desired amount and to the desired form in the joint, between the two pieces to be connected. This filler metal fuses with the melted parent metal. The molten metal, when exposed to the atmosphere, combines chemically with oxygen and nitrogen forming oxides and nitrides. This reduces its ductility and makes it less resistant to corrosion. To prevent this, the arc is shielded by an inert gas which completely envelops the molten metal and the tip of the electrode. Shielding is obtained in the manual process by the use of electrodes heavily coated with a material of such composition that large quantities of gas are produced in the heat of the arc. The coating fuses at a slower rate than the metal core, thus directing and concentrating the arc stream. The coating also forms a slag which floats on top of the molten metal, thus protecting it from the atmosphere as it cools. This slag is easily removed after the weld has cooled. Fig. 9.18 illustrates the shielded manual metal arc-welding process.

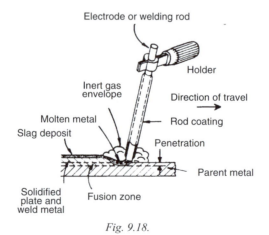

*Fig. 9.18.*

The process, as described above, will normally be used for small scale welding in the shop and on site; however, if a project is to be largely welded, then other methods of welding will be adopted. The most common are:

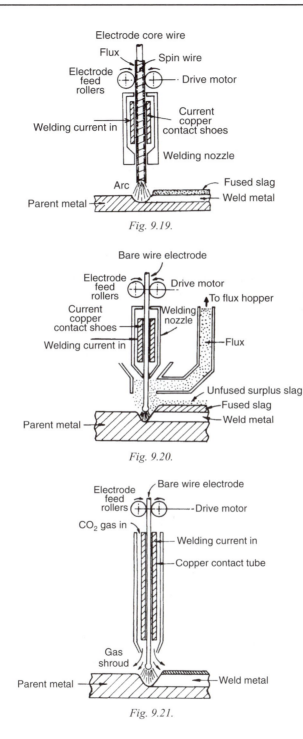

Fig. 9.19.

Fig. 9.20.

Fig. 9.21.

- Automatic welding using a continuous coated electrode.
- Submerged arc-welding (SA).
- Gas shielded welding – metal arc inert gas (MIG).

(a) In the continuous welding process, an electrode similar to that described above is fed mechanically into the weld from a coil (see Fig. 9.19). The welding head is fed along the line of the weld by means of a tractor or carriage, moved by a small electric motor at a constant speed to ensure a consistent weld. The resulting weld will be of a higher standard than the manual method and be free of the 'stop-start' points associated with the use of short manual electrodes.

(b) The submerged arc process is similar to the automatic process in that a tractor carries the welding head along the weld, but in this instance the weld metal is shielded from the air by means of a flux powder poured onto the molten metal from a hopper (see Fig. 9.20).

   The electrode in this case is not flux covered and can make direct contact in the welding head with the power supply. Once the weld is completed then the spare flux is sucked away by a vacuum cleaner, to be reused.

(c) The gas (MIG) welding process again uses a moving tractor to carry the welding head but this time the weld metal is protected by means of a stream of carbon dioxide gas which flows continuously round the weld (see Fig. 9.21). This process has very good penetration properties.

### 9.5.2. Advantages and disadvantages of welding

The practical advantages of welded structures, when compared with bolted structures are:

- Welded structures are lighter, because of the general absence of bolts, gusset plates and other joining features.
- In general, welded structures are more economical.

Cost savings arise from various factors. The general elimination of drilling for bolts permits the use of the full sectional area of a member, allowing lighter members to be used than in the corresponding bolted structures.

   Also, less time is required for detailing welded structures because connections are simplified. In addition, welded connections are well suited to structures designed in accordance with the plastic theory, which can achieve appreciable weight saving. A further cost saving may also be obtained, because savings in transportation, handling time and erection may reflect the saving in weight.

- In external work, joints can be completely sealed by welding the edges all round and so made safe against corrosion.
- Welding allows the designer greater freedom in the selection and the arrangement of the component parts of a member or structure in order to obtain the maximum efficiency from the material used.

Welding also enables sections to be built up, such as with castellated and Litzka beams, open-web girders and tapered beams. With welding, it is also possible to fabricate structures of special types such as Vierendeel trusses, orthotropic bridge decks, composite floors and tubular columns and trusses.

- Welded structures have clear surfaces and contours which result in low painting and maintenance costs.
- The rigidity of welded structures is greater than that of bolted ones.

With welding, one may attain joints of one hundred per cent efficiency, while in bolted connections the usual efficiency is around eighty per cent. With the availability of efficient rigid connections, beams can be made continuous and therefore lighter than simply-supported beams for the same purposes.

- Welding facilitates repairs, alterations and additions to existing structures.
- A welded structure may be made more aesthetically pleasing.

Among the disadvantages of welding, the following may be mentioned:

- There is a tendency for welded structures to become distorted due to the uneven heating and cooling caused by the welding. However, such distortions can generally be foreseen and largely overcome.
- More care is called for in fabrication and greater supervision is required.
- The detection of faults is more difficult and more expensive than in a bolted construction. The testing of welds may involve radiography or magnetic particle, ultrasonic or dye penetrant techniques.
- Surfaces to be welded must be clean and dry, and the achievement of these conditions presents some difficulties on site, in the wet climate of Ireland and Britain.
- After welding, it is essential to see that the weld and surrounding areas are properly cleaned and all loose material removed. The affected areas should then be given full protection against corrosion to match the remainder of the structure.
- Welding should be used with great caution in repairing or altering old structures, due to the composition of the material. In particular, structures which contain cast iron should only be welded after very careful examination as old cast iron is almost impossible to weld.

### 9.5.3. Types of weld

There are two general types of weld:

- Butt welds
- Fillet welds

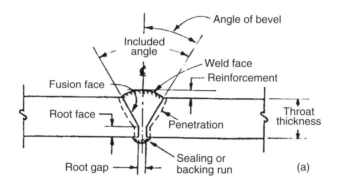

(Penetration, or depth of penetration, is that part of
the parent metal which becomes fused during welding)

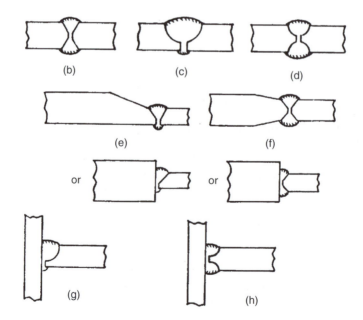

*Fig. 9.22.*

## (a) Butt welds

These are used to join steel members which are butted end to end. There are many forms or subtypes, but the more distinctive ones are possibly the following:

- Single V butt weld (see Fig. 9.22(a))
  The purpose of the V section is to allow the filler rod to be manipulated inside the V to deposit weld metal throughout the depth of the weld without difficulty.
  This type of weld is quite common with 12 mm thick plate but becomes uneconomical with plates of 25 mm thickness or more.

- Double V butt weld (Fig. 9.22(b))
  When welding can be carried out from both sides and the plates are about 25 mm thick, then the double V butt weld is used. It is not economical with plates of over 50 mm thickness.

- Single U butt weld (Fig. 9.22(c))
  Where welding can be carried out from one side only and the plates are about 25 mm thick, then the single U butt weld is used. It is not economical when the thickness of the plate is under 20 mm.

- Double U butt weld (Fig. 9.22(d))
  This weld is not recommended if the thickness of plates is below 40 mm.

- Single bevel (Fig. 9.22(e))

- Double bevel (Fig. 9.22(f))
  It is considered good practice if the thicker plate in bevel welds be given a taper of 1 in 5 to meet the thinner plate.

Other subtypes are the single J (Fig. 9.22(g)) and double J butt welds (Fig. 9.22(h)).

The size of a butt weld is specified by the throat thickness, which is normally the thickness of the thinner plate joined by the weld. The minimum penetration of a partial butt weld is given as $2\sqrt{t}$ where $t$ is the thickness of the thinner plate joined. Any eccentricities which occur from the use of partial penetration welds must be included in determining the stresses.

Permissible stresses are equal to those of the parent metal.

All important butt welds (in tension) should be fully inspected by radiography or ultrasonics to show that they are free from major defects. Some of the more important defects in butt welds are: incomplete penetration, slag inclusions, gas pockets and cracking. These can come from various sources either in the weld metal or in the heat-affected zone, adjacent to the weld, in the parent metal.

### (b) Fillet welds

These are the most commonly used welds and are used to join steel members forming a lap or T-joint.

For the general case right angle welds (90° between faces), the throat thickness is taken as 0.7 (sin 45°) of the size or leg length (see Fig. 9.23).

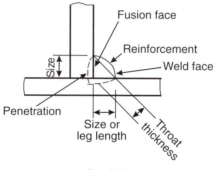

*Fig. 9.23.*

The throat thickness is used to determine the strength of the weld because a weld generally fails along a line bisecting the angle of the joint. The throat thickness does not extend to the convex surface of the weld, which is called the reinforcement, because it contains the slag of minerals other than iron that form on the surface of the molten weld metal, and are of uncertain strength.

The most commonly used sizes of fillet welds are between 6 mm and 22 mm, the larger size being used at heavily loaded connections. The welding operator can deposit welds of 10 mm and smaller in a single pass, but two or more runs are required for larger welds.

Economy can be achieved by selecting welds which require a minimum amount of metal and can be deposited in the least amount of time. As will be shown later, the strength of a fillet weld is in direct proportion to its size. However, the volume of deposited metal, and hence the cost of the weld, increases as the square of the weld size. Therefore, it is desirable to specify, when possible, a smaller but longer weld rather than a larger, shorter weld that is more costly.

The welding position must also be borne in mind; downhand welding, with the parent metal below the weld, is the fastest to execute.

Welds and welding are covered in §6.7.

The design strength, $p_w$, of a fillet weld made using covered electrodes complying with BS 639 on structural steels complying with BS EN should be obtained from BS 5950 Table 37 (Fig. 9.24), for the lowest grade of material joined.

*BS 5950 Table 37. Design strength, $p_w$*

| Grade of steel in BS EN 10025 etc. | Electrode strength to BS 639 | | | |
|---|---|---|---|---|
| | *35 N/mm²* | *42 N/mm²* | *50 N/mm²* | |
| S 275 | 220 | (220)ᵃ | (220)ᵃ | For other types of electrodes and/or other steel grades |
| S 355 | (220)ᵇ | 250 | (250)ᵃ | |
| S 460 | (220)ᵇ | (250)ᵇ | 280 | $p_w = 0.5U_e$ but $p_w \leq 0.55 U_s$ *where:* |

$U_e$ is the minimum tensile strength of the electrode, as specified in the product standard
$U_s$ is the specified minimum ultimate tensile strength of the parent metal

ᵃ Over-matching electrodes

ᵇ Under-matching electrodes. Not to be used for partial penetration butt welds

*Fig. 9.24.*

The capacity of 1 mm run of 90° fillet weld = $0.7 \times$ size $\times$ strength

The strength for grade S 275 steel is 220 N/mm²

The capacity of 1 mm run = $0.7 \times$ size $\times 220 = 154.0 \times$ size

Capacity in kN for a whole run of fillet weld

$$= \frac{154}{1\,000} \times \text{size (mm)} \times \text{effective length (mm)}$$

The effective length is the overall length minus twice the weld size. This allows for the imperfections in the welds at both ends of its run, due to the practical difficulties in starting and finishing the weld. The effective length of the weld must not be less than four times the size (leg length) of the weld.

Fig. 9.25 gives the strength for various sizes of butt and fillet welds of grade S 275 steel.

*Strength of fillet welds*

*Capacities with grade 35 electrodes to BS 639*

*Grade of steel S 275 and S 355*

| Leg length or size mm | Throat thickness mm | Capacity at 220 N/mm$^2$ kN/mm | Leg length or size mm | Throat thickness mm | Capacity at 220 N/mm$^2$ kN/mm |
|---|---|---|---|---|---|
| 3.0 | 2.1 | 0.462 | 12.0 | 8.4 | 1.85 |
| 4.0 | 2.8 | 0.616 | 15.0 | 10.5 | 2.31 |
| 5.0 | 3.5 | 0.770 | 18.0 | 12.6 | 2.77 |
| 6.0 | 4.2 | 0.924 | 20.0 | 14.0 | 3.08 |
| 8.0 | 5.6 | 1.230 | 22.0 | 15.4 | 3.39 |
| 10.0 | 7.0 | 1.540 | 25.0 | 17.5 | 3.85 |

*Strength of full penetration butt welds*

*Capacities with grade 35 electrodes to BS 639*

*Grade of steel S 275*

| Thickness mm | Shear at $0.6p_y$ kN/mm | Tension or compression at $p_y$ kN/mm | Thickness mm | Shear at $0.6p_y$ kN/mm | Tension or compression at $p_y$ kN/mm |
|---|---|---|---|---|---|
| 6.0 | 0.99 | 1.65 | 22.0 | 3.50 | 5.83 |
| 8.0 | 1.32 | 2.20 | 25.0 | 3.98 | 6.63 |
| 10.0 | 1.65 | 2.75 | 28.0 | 4.45 | 7.42 |
| 12.0 | 1.98 | 3.30 | 30.0 | 4.77 | 7.95 |
| 15.0 | 2.48 | 4.13 | 35.0 | 5.57 | 9.28 |
| 18.0 | 2.86 | 4.77 | 40.0 | 6.36 | 10.6 |
| 20.0 | 3.18 | 5.30 | 45.0 | 6.90 | 11.5 |

*Fig. 9.25.*

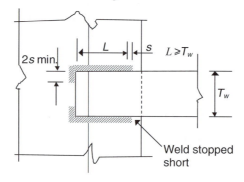

*Fig. 9.26.*

*Details of fillet welds*

*End returns.* Fillet welds finishing at the ends or sides of parts should be returned continuously around the corners for a distance of not less than twice the leg length of the weld, unless access or the configuration renders this impracticable. This detail is particularly important for fillet welds on the tension side of parts carrying a connection subject to significant moments.

*Lap joints.* In lap joints, the minimum lap should be not less than $4t$, where $t$ is the thickness of the thinner part joined. Single fillet welds should only be used where the parts are restrained to prevent opening of the joint.

*End connections.* Where the end of an element is connected only by longitudinal fillet welds, the length of the welds, $L$, should be not less than the transverse spacing, $T_w$ (see Fig. 9.26).

*Single fillet welds.* A single fillet weld should not be subject to a bending moment about the longitudinal axis of the weld.

*Intermittent fillet welds.* Intermittent fillet welds should not be used in fatigue situations or where capillary action could lead to the formation of rust pockets.

The longitudinal spacing along any one edge of the element between effective lengths of weld, as given in §6.7.2.6, should not exceed the lesser of 300 mm or $16t$ for compression elements or $24t$ for tension elements, where $t$ is the thickness of the thinner part joined.

Thin metal cannot take large currents because it burns away and thick metal rapidly conducts the heat away from the welding arc. Therefore a minimum quantity of heat is required to ensure a good weld. The alternative solution is to pre-heat the parent material to slow down the heat loss. The requirements for pre-heat are given in BS 5135, which should be consulted for general requirements for welding.

### 9.5.4. Design examples of simple welded connections

*Example 9.5.4.1. Calculate the capacity of two 12 mm thick by 100 mm wide, grade S 275 steel, tie bars, which are welded with a single V butt weld. Assume that the penetration of the weld is the full thickness of the plate.*

#### SOLUTION

Throat thickness $= 12$ mm

Design strength, $p_w = 275$ N/mm$^2$

Throat area $= 12 \times 100 = 1\,200$ mm$^2$

$$\text{Capacity} = \frac{275 \times 1200}{1000} = 330 \text{ kN}$$

*Example 9.5.4.2. Obtain the capacity of a 10 mm fillet weld, 150 mm overall length, for grade S 275 steel.*

## SOLUTION

Effective length = $150 - (2 \times 10) = 130$ mm

$$\text{Capacity} = 130 \times \frac{154 \times 10}{1000} = 200.2 \text{ kN}$$

(For strength of fillet welds, see Fig. 9.25)

*Example 9.5.4.3. Find the size of a continuous fillet weld required between the 32 mm thick flange plate and the 16 mm thick web plate of a welded plate girder, given a horizontal shear force of 1.70 kN/mm.*

## SOLUTION

Fillet welds are required on both sides of the web. Therefore, the fillet welds required on each side of the web must sustain a horizontal shear force of 0.85 kN/mm.

From Fig. 9.25, a 6 mm fillet weld will theoretically be satisfactory (0.924 kN/mm). However, because the thickness of the flange plate is 32 mm, the recommended size of the weld is 8 mm.

*Example 9.5.4.4. Find the length of the side fillet welds required for the connection shown in Fig. 9.27. The capacity of 6 mm fillet welds = 0.924 kN/mm run.*

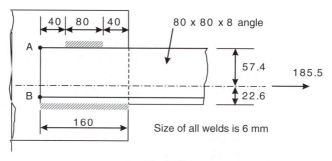

*Fig. 9.27.*

## SOLUTION

*Side B  Taking moments about A*

effective length $\times$ strength $\times$ 80 = 185.5 $\times$ 57.4

$$\text{effective length required in mm} = \frac{185.5 \times 57.4}{0.924 \times 80} = 144.0$$

overall length = 144 + (2 $\times$ 6) = 156 mm, say 160 mm

*Side A  Taking moments about B*

$$\text{effective length required} = \frac{185.5 \times 22.6}{0.924 \times 80} = 56.7$$

overall length = 56.7 + (2 $\times$ 6) = 68.7 mm

But $L \leq T_w$, $\therefore$ overall length = 80 mm

This must be positioned symmetrically, as shown in Fig. 9.27. It would, however, be common practice to make the welded length on both sides equal (see Fig. 9.26).

### 9.5.5. Welding inspection

Welding inspection is concerned primarily with the soundness and quality of a welded joint or weldment. Inspection should begin before the actual welding commences and should continue during welding as well as after it is completed. The quality of the Inspectors must be high. It goes without saying that the use of competent welders will contribute to an acceptable weld. The weld testing of structures is usually non-destructive, and includes visual, magnetic particle, radiographic, liquid penetrant and ultrasonic methods.

*Visual inspection* is simple and inexpensive. It should begin even before the first arc is struck. The materials should be examined to see that they meet the specifications for quality, type, size, cleanliness and freedom from defects. Inspections during welding may detect errors and defects that could easily be remedied. Finally, visual inspection after the weld has been completed is useful in evaluating quality, even if ultrasonic, radiographic or other methods are to be employed.

*Magnetic particle inspection* is used to detect the presence of surface cracks and discontinuities which are too fine to be seen with the naked eye, or those which lie slightly below the surface. The basic principle is that when a magnetic field is established in a piece of steel material that contains one or more discontinuities in the path of the magnetic flux, minute poles are set up at the discontinuities. These poles have a stronger attraction for the magnetic particles than the surrounding surface of the material. The particles form a pattern or indication on the surface which assumes the approximate shape of the discontinuity. It is a relatively low-cost method of inspection and is considered a very good method for detecting surface cracks.

*Radiographic inspection* is widely used for showing the presence and nature of defects and other discontinuities in the interior of the weld. This method is based on the ability of X-rays and gamma rays to penetrate metal and other opaque materials and produce an image on sensitised film or a fluorescent screen. It is a relatively expensive type of inspection and requires safety precautions due to the radiation hazard, but this method offers a permanent record when film is used.

*Liquid penetrant inspection* is used for locating cracks that are not visible to the naked eye. Fluorescent or dye penetrating substances may be used. The liquid is applied to the surface of the part to be inspected and is drawn into very small surface openings by capillary action. The excess liquid is removed from the part, a 'developer' is used to draw the penetrant to the surface, and the resulting indication is viewed. The high contrast between the liquid and the background makes possible the detection of minute traces of penetrant.

*Ultrasonic inspection* is a fast and efficient method of detecting, locating and measuring both surface and sub-surface defects in the weld and/or the base material. Ultrasonic testing makes use of an electrically timed wave of the same nature as sound waves, but of a higher pitch or frequency. The frequencies used are far above those heard by the human ear, hence, the name ultrasonic. The sound waves, or vibrations, are propagated in the metal that is being inspected until a discontinuity or change of density is reached. At these points, some of the vibrational energy is reflected back and indicated on a cathode ray tube. The pattern on the face of the tube is thus a representation of the reflected signal and of the defect.

# 10. Portal frame design

## 10.1. Introduction

The most common form of structural arrangement for single-storey build-ings is that of portal frame construction. The modern portal frame is basically a rigidly-jointed plane frame made from hot-rolled sections, supporting the roofing and side cladding via cold-formed purlins, and sheeting rails. A typical, two bay, industrial building is shown in Fig. 10.1. Nowadays, typical spans of portal frames are in the region of 30 m to 40 m, though spans can vary from 15 m to 80 m. The common spacing between frames is about 6 m, but can vary from about 4.5 m to 10.0 m, depending to some extent on the span of the frames. The height to the lowest part of the roof member in a normal industrial building is usually of the order of 4.5 m

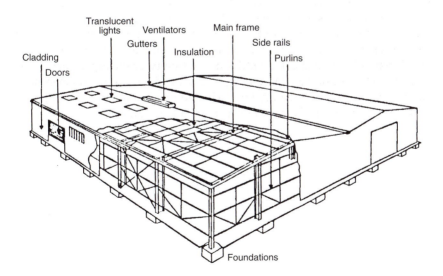

*Fig. 10.1.*

to 6.0 m. Such frames are economical when covering large clear floor areas, thus offering maximum adaptability of the space inside the building.

The setting out of portal frames as envisaged by BS 5950 may be seen in Figs. 17 and 18 in the code, but see the comment on $L_b$ in the section on stability.

## 10.2. Behaviour of a portal frame at failure

The behaviour of a portal frame at failure must be considered first before undertaking the design of the frame in detail. The case of a frame subjected to uniform dead and imposed loads is considered here (see Fig. 10.2). The total load is assumed to be steadily increasing until ultimate failure of the structure occurs.

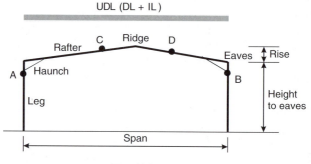

*Fig. 10.2.*

The first part of the loading will be within the elastic limits of the steel and the behaviour of the frame will be very nearly linear; the deflection will be very close to being proportional to the applied load. It will also be found that if the load is removed then the structure will return to its original shape. During this part of the loading, the forces in the frame may be calculated using elastic methods, either by hand or, for complicated frames, by a computer. At any point on the frame the value of $M/M_p$ may be calculated, where $M$ is the applied moment and $M_p$ the plastic moment capacity of the section.

The first plastic hinge in the structure will occur at the first point in the frame where the $M/M_p$ ratio reaches 1.0. Once this point has been established, it becomes necessary to determine the next point to become a plastic hinge. This is done by re-analysing the frame with the moment fixed at the plastic hinge position, its value being the plastic moment capacity of the member's section. Again, there will be another point where the value of $M/M_p$ will reach 1.0. This will then become the second hinge position.

Further hinge positions will be found until the frame becomes a mechanism at the ultimate load-carrying capacity of the frame.

For standard portal frames, the positions of the plastic hinges can be determined in advance. In simple design cases, it is recommended that the hinges should be at the bottom of the haunch and in the rafter near the ridge. This is shown in Fig. 10.2 where the hinges are assumed to be at points A, B, C and D. It is important that the engineer also checks the effects of wind loading on the structure, because there could be a possible change in the position of hinge locations, and stress reversal.

It will be noticed that there are many ridge portal frames built which are symmetrical and have uniform loading. The apparent number of hinges which seem to be needed exceed the number which would normally be expected in conventional elastic analysis, and yet there is no premature failure. This may be explained by considering the frame in Fig. 10.2. If the first hinges notionally form in the legs at points A and B, then it would appear that the frame has failed, but due to the normal imperfections present in the structure, the frame will sway. When this happens, the moment in one of the hinges will be reduced and it will lock, thus forming a solid member. It will then be necessary to continue loading until another hinge forms in the frame before failure occurs.

Once the collapse mode has been fully determined and the plastic hinge positions found, a check should be made to ensure that the lowest failure load has been obtained. The easiest way to do this is to draw a moment diagram of the frame, in order to ensure that premature failure will not occur; the value of $M/M_p$ should be checked at all points on the frame. In most practical cases of portal frames this can be carried out by inspection. If the lowest bound solution has been found, then the moments will be equal to the plastic moment capacities at plastic hinges and less at all other points on the frame. If the plastic moment capacity has been exceeded at any other point on the frame, then the lowest bound solution has not been found and a revised set of plastic hinge positions will need to be considered.

## 10.3. Moment diagrams

The construction of the moment diagrams mentioned in the previous section can be undertaken in the following stages:

- Draw the free moment diagram assuming that there are sufficient releases to produce a statically determinate structure.
- Draw reactant diagrams from the unknown forces, which may well have to be determined.
- Draw the final combined diagram for the structure, using the free moment diagram and the reactant diagram.

Taking each of these in turn for a simple portal frame gives the following steps:

(a) The diagram for the vertical forces only is drawn, assuming that one of the feet of the frame is on rollers and the frame is therefore free to spread. It is usual to plot the diagram on a developed single line frame drawing (see Fig. 10.3). The numeric values for the various points in the diagram are obtained from the equation for a free moment curve. At any point $x$, the value is $wxL/2 - wx^2/2$, with a maximum value at the centre of the span of $wL^2/8$. Note that the moments in the legs for this case are zero.

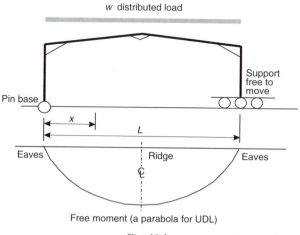

Fig. 10.3.

(b) When erected, the frame is constrained against spreading at the feet by the foundations. Therefore there is an additional horizontal force ($H$) applied to the frame. This force generates another moment diagram shown in Fig. 10.4. Taking the horizontal force and multiplying it by the height above the base gives the moment at any point in the frame, in this case.

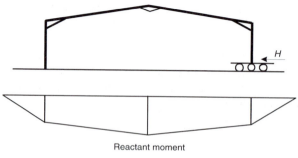

Reactant moment

Fig. 10.4.

(c) The two diagrams may then be combined to give the final moment diagram on the frame (see Fig. 10.5). The moment due to the horizontal reaction at the feet will reduce the free moment in the rafter. Plastic hinges will form at the points where the solid vertical lines are shown, i.e. at the bottom of the haunch in the legs and at the top of the rafter near the ridge.

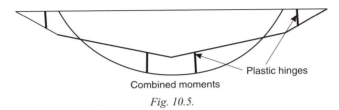

Plastic hinges

Combined moments

*Fig. 10.5.*

If all the procedures have been followed correctly, it will be found that the moment will be equal to $M_p$ where the maximum moments occur and less at all other points.

Note: The same result may be obtained by using virtual work equations.

There are, in fact, several different manual methods for analysing portal frames, i.e. graphical, semi-graphical, mechanism method and plastic moment distribution. There are also a number of commercially-available computer design packages.

## 10.4. Frame equilibrium

The use of plastic design will not invalidate the normal requirements of equilibrium, which means that all the internal forces and moments must balance the external applied loads. Because the strength of the section is fully utilised at the plastic hinges in resisting the applied moments, the internal moments are already known at these points. Because of this, it is frequently possible to construct the reactant and final moment diagrams for simple frames without recourse to the analytical techniques normally used for indeterminate structures. This procedure may be illustrated by considering the equilibrium at the hinge locations in the typical portal frame already considered.

Consider the hinge in the leg (Fig. 10.6). The moment at the bottom of the haunch will be the plastic moment capacity of the section. This will cause a horizontal force at the foot of the frame equal to the moment divided by the height to the hinge position ($h_1$).

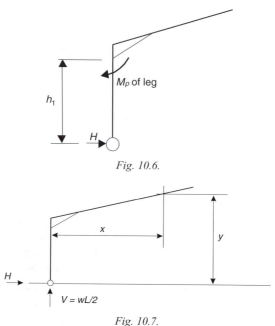

*Fig. 10.6.*

*Fig. 10.7.*

Consider the hinge in the rafter near the ridge (Fig. 10.7). As with the leg hinge, the moment will be equal to the plastic moment of the section which must be balanced by the external applied forces, including the reactions at the foot of the frame. In this case the following equation can be used:

$$w \times L/2 - Hy - wx^2/2 = M_p \text{ rafter}$$

The use of this equation provides a ready means of calculating both the moments in the frame and the minimum plastic moments required for each section. It should be noted that the point of maximum moment in the rafter is not at the ridge, unless the rafter is horizontal. The exact location depends on the geometry of the frame, see Graph 10.4.

## 10.5. Frame stability

During loading, all structures move a certain amount. At times this movement will cause the structure to lose some of its strength. When this happens, an allowance must be made for the effect in the design procedure. For portal frames, designed to BS 5950, this is carried out by checking if the frame is sensitive to sway. The check is detailed in §5.5.4.2, which gives two methods of checking sway stability. The first is to apply a lateral load to the frame equal to 0.5 per cent of the factored vertical dead and imposed loads and calculate the resulting elastic deflection which must not exceed the height of the columns divided by 1 000. The second method is to use a stability formula which is given as:

$$\frac{L_b}{D} \le \frac{44}{\Omega} \frac{L}{h} \left( \frac{\varrho}{4 + \varrho L_r / L} \right) \left( \frac{275}{p_{yr}} \right)$$

where:

$$\varrho = \left( \frac{2I_c}{I_r} \right) \left( \frac{L}{h} \right) \text{ for a single bay frame}$$

$$\varrho = \left( \frac{I_c}{I_r} \right) \left( \frac{L}{h} \right) \text{ for a multi-bay frame}$$

$L$ is the span of the bay

$L_b$ is the effective span of the bay

$$L_b = L - \left( \frac{2D_h}{D_s + D_h} \right) L_h$$

where:

$D_h$ is the additional depth of the haunch

$D_s$ is the depth of the rafter, allowing for its slope

$L_h$ is the length of a haunch

(See Fig. 17 of BS 5950 and Fig. 10.8(a))

$D$ is the minimum cross-section depth of the rafters

$h$ is the mean column height

$I_c$ is the minimum second moment of area of the column for bending in the plane of the frame (taken as zero if the column is not rigidly connected to the rafter)

$I_r$ is the minimum second moment of area of the rafters for bending in the plane of the frame

$p_{yr}$ is the design strength of the rafters

$L_r$ is the total developed length of the rafter in the bay

$\Omega$ is the arching ratio, $W_r/W_o$

$W_o$ is the value of $W_r$ for plastic failure of the rafters as a fixed-ended beam of span $L$

$W_r$ is the total factored vertical load on the rafters of the bay

If either the sway check or the equation are satisfied then the frame may be assumed to be stable for gravity loads but the critical load factor, $\lambda_r$, must be derived for load cases including horizontal forces.

$$\lambda_r = \frac{\lambda_{sc}}{\lambda_{sc} - 1}$$

where:

$$\lambda_{sc} = \frac{h}{200\delta_i}$$

$\delta_i$ is the deflection due to the notional horizontal load

$h_i$ is the height of the column

If the deflection is not calculated then the value of $\lambda_{sc}$ may be obtained from the following equation, providing there are no significant point or gantry loads:

$$\lambda_{sc} = \frac{220DL}{\Omega hL_b}\left(\frac{\varrho}{4 + \varrho L_r/L}\right)\left(\frac{275}{p_{yr}}\right)$$

It is recommended that this check, and any subsequent changes on the chosen frame, be made before any other calculations are performed.

In addition to the general stability of the frame as a whole, the stability of each member must also be considered as follows:

- Stability at plastic hinges. This has already been mentioned in Chapter 5 of this book.
- The distance to the first restraint away from the hinge position. The equation given in Chapter 5 may be used, but when there is adequate restraint on the tension flange the formulae in §5.3.4 and Annex G may be invoked. These give much greater distances to the next restraint and therefore economy in design.
- The remainder of the frame, where the rules given for unrestrained members can be used to ensure that the frame is stable.
- Local buckling, which should be considered when selecting a section. A more detailed discussion has already been given in Section 5.6 of this book. For areas where plastic hinges occur, the section must be a class 1 type of section, i.e. one suitable for plastic design. This may influence the choice of section, particularly when using steels with a higher yield stress than S 275 steels.

## 10.6. Member proportions and haunch length

The determination of member sizes is a matter of judgement and experience, although some help has been provided to the engineer by various authors (see bibliography). In addition to the help given in these references, most engineers develop their own methods of determining section sizes. It should be recognised that the material available in a stock yard may well be a determining factor in the sections chosen!

For the purposes of this book, it will be assumed that the sections will be selected using graphs similar to those later in this chapter. These graphs are intended for preliminary assessment of the member sizes and are based on the following assumptions:

- There is a plastic hinge in the leg at the top of the haunch.
- There is a second hinge in the rafter at a point determined from the frame geometry.
- The haunch is 10 per cent of the span in length.
- The loading on the rafter is uniform.
- The depth of the rafter is 1/50 of the span.

The four graphs give:

10.1 The horizontal force at the foot of the frame.
10.2 The moment in the rafter.
10.3 The moment in the leg.
10.4 The distance from the centre of a column to the point of maximum moment in the adjacent rafter.

It must be noted that these graphs are intended for preliminary member sizing and that a full check is required on the members once the initial dimensions have been determined.

The haunch is provided to ease the design and construction of the connection and to provide economy by reducing the size of the rafter.

The connection involves making a full strength joint between the rafter and the leg to develop a plastic moment. In order to obtain a practical number and layout of bolts, it is necessary to increase the lever arm in the connection. Also, if a deeper haunch section takes the maximum moment in the rafter, which occurs at the eaves, then a lighter rafter may be used. These two considerations lead to the provision of a haunch (see Fig. 10.8(a)).

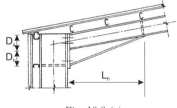

*Fig. 10.8 (a)*

A common way to form the material for the haunch is to take a length of the rafter section and make a diagonal cut along the section. The splayed web is then welded to the underside of the rafter to form the haunch (see Fig. 10.8(b)).

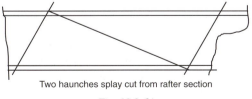

Two haunches splay cut from rafter section

*Fig. 10.8 (b)*

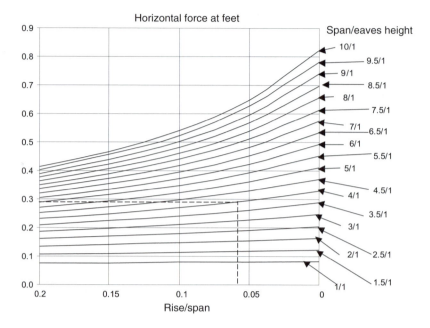

*Graph 10.1.*

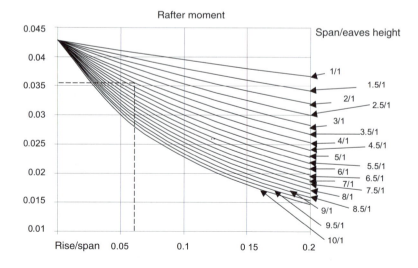

*Graph 10.2.*

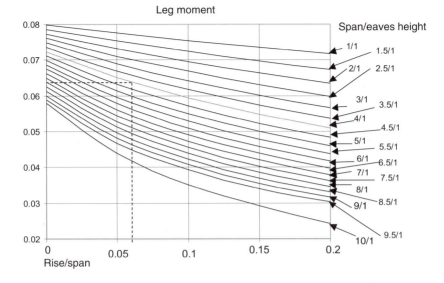

*Graph 10.3.*

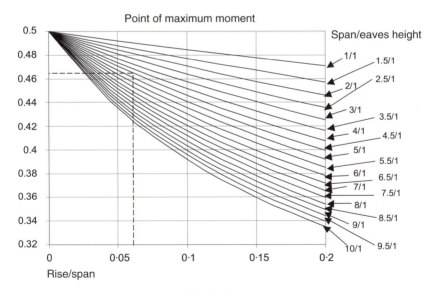

*Graph 10.4.*

There is a practical maximum length for the haunch to ensure that there are no problems with stability. This is usually taken as ten per cent of the span; if the haunch is longer then there will be a long compression flange to stabilise and there will also be a risk of creating plastic lengths instead of hinges within the haunch. From an economic point of view, too long a haunch will give a much longer length of weld needed to join the web of the haunch to the underside of the rafter.

## 10.7. Apex or ridge connection

The moment at the apex is usually less than the full plastic capacity of the section and a simple site joint will be sufficient.

For practical reasons and ease of erection and alignment, at least four bolts are provided (see Fig. 10.9(a)).

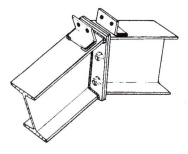

*Fig. 10.9 (a)*

Other typical details of apex connections are shown in Fig. 10.9(b).

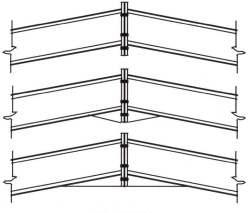

*Fig. 10.9 (b)*

## 10.8. Design of a typical portal frame

A typical ridge-type portal frame is shown in Fig. 10.10.

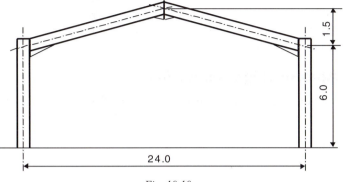

*Fig. 10.10.*

*Example 10.8.1. A ridge-type portal frame has a span of 24 m, a height to eaves of 6 m, and a rise of 1.5 m. The frames, spaced at 6 m centres, are to support 0.75 kN/m² imposed and 0.45 kN/m² dead load, including the self-weight of the frame. Design the frame in grade S 275 steel, assuming that the DL + IL case is the design criterion.*

*SOLUTION*

$$DL = 0.45 \text{ kN/m}^2$$

$$IL = 0.75 \text{ kN/m}^2$$

The frame DL $= 0.45 \times 6 = 2.7$ kN/m

The factored DL $= 2.7 \times 1.4 = 3.78$ kN/m

Total DL $= 3.78 \times 24 = 90.72$ kN

The frame IL $= 0.75 \times 6 = 4.5$ kN/m

The factored IL $= 4.5 \times 1.6 = 7.2$ kN/m

Total IL $= 7.2 \times 24 = 172.8$ kN

Total DL + IL $= 263.52$ kN

Using graphs, the following parameters are required:

(a) Total load on the frame, as shown above = 263.52 kN
(b) Total load $\times$ span $= 263.52 \times 24 = 6\,324$ kNm

(c) Span/Eaves height = 24/6 = 4
(d) Rise/span = 1.5/24 = 0.0625

The following values may be read from the graphs:

(a) Horizontal force at the foot of the frame (graph 10.1)
$0.288 \times 263.52 = 76$ kN
(b) Plastic moment required in the rafter (graph 10.2)
$0.0355 \times 6\,324 = 224.5$ kNm
(c) Plastic moment required in the leg (graph 10.3)
$0.0643 \times 6\,324 = 406.6$ kNm
(d) The point of maximum moment in the rafter (graph 10.4)
$0.47 \times 20 = 9.4$ m
It should be noted that if the rise is high compared to the span then the point of maximum moment can move a significant distance from the centre of the frame.

The plastic modulus required for each section is the moment derived from the above calculations divided by the design strength.

In this case, it will be assumed that the design strength will be 275 N/mm$^2$ as the section flanges will almost certainly be less than 16 mm thick.

Taking each member in turn:

Rafter moment = 224.5 kNm
$S_x$ required = $224.5 \times 10^3/275 = 817$ cm$^3$

Leg moment = 406.6 kNm
$S_x$ required = $406.6 \times 10^3/275 = 1\,479$ cm$^3$

The following satisfies these:

Rafters
$406 \times 140 \times 46$ UB, (plastic modulus = 888 cm$^3$)

Legs
$457 \times 152 \times 74$ UB, (plastic modulus 1 627 cm$^3$)

### Check on sway stability

These members will be satisfactory if the frame is not free to sway. It must now be checked to see if it is stable when free. This may be carried out by an elastic analysis with a nominal load, as already described, or the check may be made using a formula in the code. It should be noted that certain types of frame require a more detailed check on stability, using second order analysis. For this example the code formula will be used.

The formula has already been given earlier in the text, so the various factors will now be calculated, starting with the left-hand side (evaluating $L_b/D$).

In this case:

$L_b = 24 - 2.4 = 21.6$ m

$D = 403.2$ mm

$L_b/D = 21.6 \times 10^3/403.2 = 53.6$, which must be less than the right-hand side of the equation.

In evaluating the right-hand side of the expression, several terms must be derived before the whole equation may be evaluated.

Taking each of these in turn:

$$\varrho = \left(\frac{2I_c}{I_r}\right)\left(\frac{L}{h}\right)$$

$$\left(\frac{2 \times 32\,670}{15\,690}\right)\left(\frac{24}{6}\right) = 16.7$$

$W_0$ = applied load/load capacity as fixed-ended beam

$$M_p = \frac{275 \times 888}{10^3} = 244 \text{ kNm}$$

Load as fixed ended beam $= 16 \times \dfrac{M_p}{\text{span}}$

$$= 16 \times \frac{244}{24} = 162.7 \text{ kN}$$

$$\therefore \Omega = \frac{W_r}{W_o} = \frac{263.52}{162.7} = 1.62$$

$$L_r = 2 \times \left(12^2 + 1.5^2\right)^{0.5} = 24.2 \text{ m}$$

The right-hand side of the expression can now be evaluated:

$$\frac{44}{1.62} \times \frac{24}{6} \times \frac{(16.7)}{\left(4 + 16.7 \times 24.2/24\right)} \times \frac{275}{275} = 87.1$$

As the right-hand side of the expression is greater than the left, the frame is stable against the possibility of sway failure. Had this not been the case, the rafter or leg would have had to be increased to ensure such stability; it is for this reason that the sway check should be carried out first.

*Stanchion stability*

It is assumed that the leg will be held in place at the plastic hinge position, as recommended in §5.3.2 for an effective means of providing this restraint.

This means that both flanges must be held rigidly against lateral movement by some suitable means. These restraints must not only be rigid, but must also be capable of resisting a force equal to 2.5% of the axial compression force in the flanges. Any suitable bracing which meets these requirements may be used.

The leg should then be restrained at a distance down the leg from the hinge restraint not greater than the value $L_m$ given in the earlier discussion on plastic design. The procedure is as follows:

a. Average stress in the column $= \dfrac{\text{load}}{\text{area}} = \dfrac{(263.52 \times 10/2)}{94.5} = 13.9$ N/mm$^2$, say 14 N/mm$^2$.
b. The value of $x$, which can be read from the section tables, is 30.1.
c. The value of $r_y$, which can be read from the section tables, is 3.33 cm.
d. The design strength, which in this case is 275 N/mm$^2$

Substituting these values in the equation:

$$L_m \leq \frac{38 r_y}{\left[ \left( \dfrac{f_c}{130} \right) + \left( \dfrac{p_y}{275} \right)^2 \left( \dfrac{x}{36} \right)^2 \right]^{0.5}}$$

$$L_m \leq \frac{38 \times 3.33/100}{\left( \dfrac{14}{130} + \left( \dfrac{275}{275} \right)^2 \left( \dfrac{30.1}{36} \right)^2 \right)^{0.5}} = 1.409 \text{ m}$$

The first restraint below the haunch will, therefore, be 1.409 m below the hinge position.

In many cases, the outside of the frame will have sheeting rails at about 1.5 m centres to carry the vertical cladding. When this happens, advantage may be taken of the restraint provided by the rails, assuming they are firmly fixed to the leg. In this case, §5.3.4 may be invoked to calculate the maximum distance between the restraints to the compression flange. This clause gives an equation for the maximum distances, assuming restraint to the tension flange. The equations are derived from the method given in Annex G of BS 5950. The reader must study the requirements given in §5.3.4 as it is necessary to comply with them if this method is to be used.

In this case the maximum distance to the next restraint is given as:

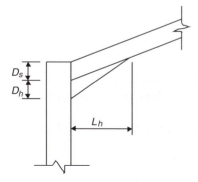

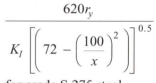

$$\frac{620 r_y}{K_1 \left[ \left( 72 - \left( \frac{100}{x} \right)^2 \right) \right]^{0.5}}$$

for grade S 275 steel

Where $K_1$ has the following values:

Un-haunched segment $K_1 = 1$

$D_h/D_s = 1 \qquad K_1 = 1.25$

$D_h/D_s = 2 \qquad K_1 = 1.40$

The method may be applied to a leg as well as a rafter. This results in a maximum distance for this leg of:

$$\frac{620 \times 3.33 \times 10}{1.0 \times \left( 72 - \left( \frac{100}{30.1} \right)^2 \right)^{0.5}} = 2644 \text{ mm or } 2.644 \text{ m}$$

The torsional index for this section ($x$) is 30.1.

It will be noticed that when the tension flange is held, there is a great gain to be found in the leg stability. If this assumption is made then it is essential that the engineer checks that there are no door or window openings which inhibit the provision of restraint on the external flanges.

### Rafter stability

The rafter must also be checked to find the maximum spacing of the restraints, both at the plastic hinge positions and along the rest of its length. Considering the plastic hinge position first. The limits are calculated in the same way as for the leg without taking the restraint on the tension flange into account.

For the rafter, the value of $r_y = 30.3$ mm and the value of $x = 38.9$.

The compression force in the rafter is normally small and will not be considered in this case. This reduces the formula to:

$$L_m \leq \frac{38 r_y}{\left[ \left( \frac{p_y}{275} \right)^2 \left( \frac{x}{36} \right)^2 \right]^{0.5}}$$

$$L_m = \frac{38 \times 30.3}{\left[\left(\frac{275}{275}\right)^2\left(\frac{38.9}{36}\right)^2\right]^{0.5}} = 1065 \text{ mm or } 1.065 \text{ m}$$

The rafter away from the plastic position is treated using the rules given in §4.3, which have already been discussed.

### Haunch stability

The stability of the haunch may be calculated using the simple, but slightly conservative, rules given in §5.3.4 of BS 5950 or may be checked from the rules in Annex G of BS 5950. For this example, the rules in §5.3.4 will be adopted. Using the equation given in the checks on the frame legs and substituting the values for the rafter, as given in the code, the maximum distance between the restraints is:

$$\frac{620 \times 3.03 \times 10}{1.25 \times \left[72 - \left(\frac{100}{38.9}\right)^2\right]^{0.5}} = 1859 \text{ mm or } 1.859 \text{ m}$$

As the haunch will be 2.4 m long, this means that the haunch must be restrained at 1.85 m from the face of the leg, and again at a point about 1.85 m further along the haunch. An improved spacing may be obtained by using the rules in Annex G of BS 5950.

### Frame stability

The structure must not be capable of becoming a mechanism in both the longitudinal and transverse directions during erection and use. The possibility of the gable end deflecting at the ridge due to wind loading on the gable end must also be considered (see Fig. 10.11).

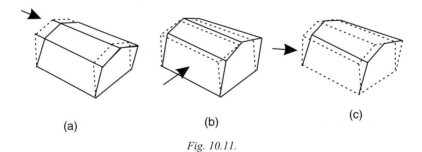

(a)    (b)    (c)

*Fig. 10.11.*

The portal frame will provide transverse stiffness to the structure when it is complete and the haunch and ridge joints are bolted up. The longitudinal stability will be provided by vertical bracing in the side walls between the stanchions of the portal frames. The effects of the wind on the gable ends can be accommodated by the use of rafter bracing fixed under the purlins. It is recommended that the bracing is placed in one bay from ridge to foundations, rather than bracing one bay in the roof and another in the side walls. Fig. 10.12 shows the end of a typical portal frame.

Often it will be found that in buildings with two or more bays the valley stanchions will need to be braced, but the client may not permit the obstruction to the free use of the building caused by the bracing. In these cases, one solution is to provide the longitudinal strength required for stability by adding a rectangular portal frame into the line of the valley.

The vertical bracing may not always be in the end, or ultimate, bay of the structure. The reason for this is twofold:

- To reduce the concentrated stresses in the end bay due to a fixed gable wall adjacent to a relatively less stiff portal frame.
- The end bay of the structure is frequently used as an entrance, and provision must be made for a door opening, which would be obstructed by the bracing.

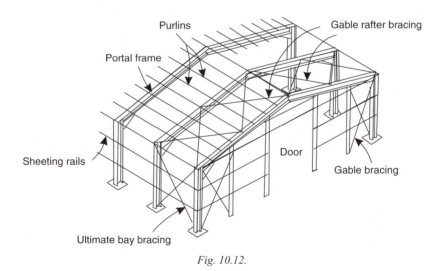

*Fig. 10.12.*

In both these cases, the bracing will be moved to the penultimate bay (see Fig. 10.1). In very long buildings, the bracing may also be used in internal bays to provide additional stiffness, especially if an expansion joint is required in the structure. For structures over a certain length (usually about 60 m), the provision of expansion joints is needed to reduce the thermal stresses which arise from the changes in temperature, unless these are included in the design.

# Appendix A

**Useful formulae for beams**

## SIMPLY SUPPORTED BEAMS

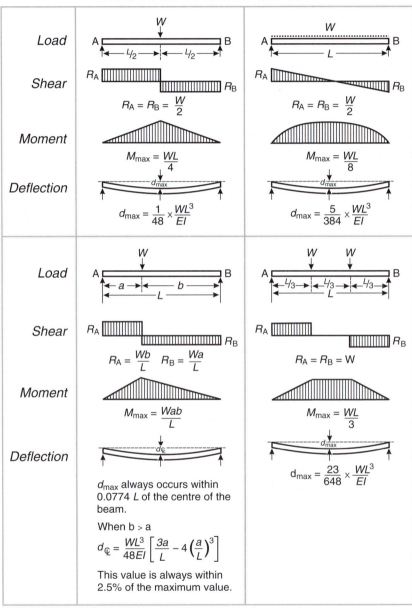

**Load**

$R_A = R_B = \dfrac{W}{2}$

**Shear**

$R_A = R_B = \dfrac{W}{2}$

**Moment**

$M_{max} = \dfrac{WL}{4}$

$M_{max} = \dfrac{WL}{8}$

**Deflection**

$d_{max} = \dfrac{1}{48} \times \dfrac{WL^3}{EI}$

$d_{max} = \dfrac{5}{384} \times \dfrac{WL^3}{EI}$

**Load**

**Shear**

$R_A = \dfrac{Wb}{L} \quad R_B = \dfrac{Wa}{L}$

$R_A = R_B = W$

**Moment**

$M_{max} = \dfrac{Wab}{L}$

$M_{max} = \dfrac{WL}{3}$

**Deflection**

$d_{max}$ always occurs within 0.0774 $L$ of the centre of the beam.

When b > a

$d_{\mathbb{C}} = \dfrac{WL^3}{48EI} \left[ \dfrac{3a}{L} - 4\left(\dfrac{a}{L}\right)^3 \right]$

This value is always within 2.5% of the maximum value.

$d_{max} = \dfrac{23}{648} \times \dfrac{WL^3}{EI}$

# FIXED ENDED (OR BUILT-IN) BEAMS

|  | | |
|---|---|---|
| *Load* | | |
| *Shear* | $R_A = R_B = \dfrac{W}{2}$ | $R_A = R_B = \dfrac{W}{2}$ |
| *Moment* | $M_A = M_B = M_C = \dfrac{WL}{8}$ | $M_A = M_B = \dfrac{WL}{12}$ <br> $M_C = \dfrac{WL}{24}$ |
| *Deflection* | $d_{max} = \dfrac{1}{192} \times \dfrac{WL^3}{EI}$ | $d_{max} = \dfrac{1}{384} \times \dfrac{WL^3}{EI}$ |
| *Load* | | |
| *Shear* | $R_A = W\left(\dfrac{b}{L}\right)^2\left(1 + 2\dfrac{a}{L}\right)$ <br> $R_B = W\left(\dfrac{a}{L}\right)^2\left(1 + 2\dfrac{b}{L}\right)$ | $R_A = R_B = W$ |
| *Moment* | $M_A = \dfrac{Wab^2}{L^2} \quad M_B = \dfrac{Wba^2}{L^2}$ <br> $M_C = \dfrac{2Wa^2b^2}{L^3}$ | $M_A = M_B = \dfrac{2WL}{9}$ <br> $M_C = M_D = \dfrac{WL}{9}$ |
| *Deflection* | $d_{max} = \dfrac{2Wa^2b^3}{3EI(3L - 2a)^2}$ <br> when $x = \dfrac{L^2}{3L - 2a}$ <br> $d_C = \dfrac{Wa^3b^3}{3EIL^3}$ | $d_{max} = \dfrac{5}{648} \times \dfrac{WL^3}{EI}$ |

## CANTILEVERS

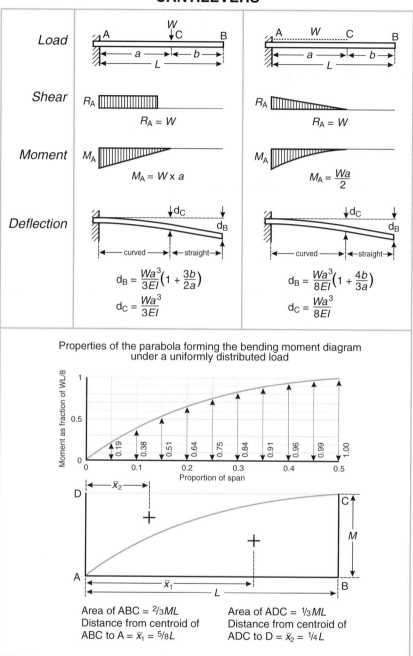

**Load**

**Shear** $R_A = W$

**Moment** $M_A = W \times a$ ; $M_A = \dfrac{Wa}{2}$

**Deflection**

$$d_B = \frac{Wa^3}{3EI}\left(1 + \frac{3b}{2a}\right)$$

$$d_C = \frac{Wa^3}{3EI}$$

$$d_B = \frac{Wa^3}{8EI}\left(1 + \frac{4b}{3a}\right)$$

$$d_C = \frac{Wa^3}{8EI}$$

Properties of the parabola forming the bending moment diagram
under a uniformly distributed load

Moment as fraction of WL/8

0.19  0.38  0.51  0.64  0.75  0.84  0.91  0.96  0.99  1.00

Proportion of span

Area of ABC = $^2/_3 ML$
Distance from centroid of
ABC to A = $\bar{x}_1 = {}^5/_8 L$

Area of ADC = $^1/_3 ML$
Distance from centroid of
ADC to D = $\bar{x}_2 = {}^1/_4 L$

# Appendix B

## Universal beam section properties

*The following eight pages form one large table. The depth of the table can be seen in the even pages 234, 236, 238 and 240. The width of the table can be seen in facing pairs of even and odd pages; thus pages 234 and 235 form the whole width and one quarter of the whole table.*

*This table is completed on the opposite page*

| Designation | Mass per metre | Depth of section | Width of section | Thickness web | Thickness flange | Root radius | Depth between fillets | Ratios for local buckling | | Second moment of area | |
|---|---|---|---|---|---|---|---|---|---|---|---|
| | | D | B | t | T | r | d | Flange B/2T | Web d/t | X–X | Y–Y |
| | kg/m | mm | mm | mm | mm | mm | mm | | | cm⁴ | cm⁴ |
| 914 × 419 × 388 | 388.0 | 921.0 | 420.5 | 21.4 | 36.6 | 24.1 | 799.6 | 5.74 | 37.4 | 719600 | 45440 |
| 914 × 419 × 343 | 343.3 | 911.8 | 418.5 | 19.4 | 32.0 | 24.1 | 799.6 | 6.54 | 41.2 | 625800 | 39160 |
| 914 × 305 × 289 | 289.1 | 926.6 | 307.7 | 19.5 | 32.0 | 19.1 | 824.4 | 4.81 | 42.3 | 504200 | 15600 |
| 914 × 305 × 253 | 253.4 | 918.4 | 305.5 | 17.3 | 27.9 | 19.1 | 824.4 | 5.47 | 47.7 | 436300 | 13300 |
| 914 × 305 × 224 | 224.2 | 910.4 | 304.1 | 15.9 | 23.9 | 19.1 | 824.4 | 6.36 | 51.8 | 376400 | 11240 |
| 914 × 305 × 201 | 200.9 | 903.0 | 303.3 | 15.1 | 20.2 | 19.1 | 824.4 | 7.51 | 54.6 | 325300 | 9423 |
| 838 × 292 × 226 | 226.5 | 850.9 | 293.8 | 16.1 | 26.8 | 17.8 | 761.7 | 5.48 | 47.3 | 339700 | 11360 |
| 838 × 292 × 194 | 193.8 | 840.7 | 292.4 | 14.7 | 21.7 | 17.8 | 761.7 | 6.74 | 51.8 | 279200 | 9066 |
| 838 × 292 × 176 | 175.9 | 834.9 | 291.7 | 14.0 | 18.8 | 17.8 | 761.7 | 7.76 | 54.4 | 246000 | 7799 |
| 762 × 267 × 197 | 196.8 | 769.8 | 268.0 | 15.6 | 25.4 | 16.5 | 686.0 | 5.28 | 44.0 | 240000 | 8175 |
| 762 × 267 × 173 | 173.0 | 762.2 | 266.7 | 14.3 | 21.6 | 16.5 | 686.0 | 6.17 | 48.0 | 205300 | 6650 |
| 762 × 267 × 147 | 146.9 | 754.0 | 265.2 | 12.8 | 17.5 | 16.5 | 686.0 | 7.58 | 53.6 | 168500 | 5455 |
| 762 × 267 × 134 | 133.9 | 750.0 | 264.4 | 12.0 | 15.5 | 16.5 | 686.0 | 8.53 | 57.2 | 150700 | 4788 |
| 686 × 254 × 170 | 170.2 | 692.9 | 255.8 | 14.5 | 23.7 | 15.2 | 615.1 | 5.40 | 42.4 | 170300 | 6630 |
| 686 × 254 × 152 | 152.4 | 687.5 | 254.5 | 13.2 | 21.0 | 15.2 | 615.1 | 8.06 | 46.6 | 150400 | 5784 |
| 686 × 254 × 140 | 140.1 | 663.5 | 253.7 | 12.4 | 19.0 | 15.2 | 615.1 | 6.68 | 49.6 | 136300 | 5183 |
| 686 × 254 × 125 | 125.2 | 677.9 | 253.0 | 11.7 | 16.2 | 15.2 | 615.1 | 7.81 | 52.6 | 118000 | 4383 |
| 610 × 305 × 238 | 238.1 | 635.8 | 311.4 | 18.4 | 31.4 | 16.5 | 540.0 | 4.96 | 29.3 | 209500 | 15840 |
| 610 × 305 × 179 | 179.0 | 620.2 | 307.1 | 14.1 | 23.6 | 16.5 | 540.0 | 6.51 | 38.3 | 153000 | 11410 |

*This table continues on page 236*

| Radius of gyration | | Elastic modulus | | Plastic modulus | | Buckling parameter index *u* | Torsional index *x* | Warping constant *H dm⁶* | Torsional constant *J cm⁴* | Area *cm²* | Mass *kg/m* | Designation |
|---|---|---|---|---|---|---|---|---|---|---|---|---|
| 9.59 | 38.2 | 15630 | 2161 | 17670 | 3341 | 0.885 | 26.7 | 88.9 | 1734 | 494 | 388.0 | 914 × 419 × 388 |
| 9.46 | 37.8 | 13730 | 1871 | 15480 | 2890 | 0.883 | 30.1 | 75.8 | 1193 | 437 | 343.3 | 914 × 419 × 343 |
| 6.51 | 37.0 | 10880 | 1014 | 12570 | 1601 | 0.867 | 31.9 | 31.2 | 926 | 368 | 289.1 | 914 × 305 × 289 |
| 6.42 | 36.8 | 9501 | 871 | 10940 | 1371 | 0.866 | 36.2 | 26.4 | 626 | 323 | 253.4 | 914 × 305 × 253 |
| 6.27 | 36.3 | 8269 | 739 | 9535 | 1163 | 0.861 | 41.3 | 22.1 | 422 | 286 | 224.2 | 914 × 305 × 224 |
| 6.07 | 35.7 | 7204 | 621 | 8351 | 982 | 0.854 | 46.8 | 18.4 | 291 | 256 | 200.9 | 914 × 305 × 201 |
| 6.27 | 34.3 | 7985 | 773 | 9155 | 1212 | 0.870 | 35.0 | 19.3 | 514 | 289 | 226.5 | 838 × 292 × 226 |
| 6.06 | 33.6 | 6641 | 620 | 7640 | 974 | 0.862 | 41.6 | 15.2 | 306 | 247 | 193.8 | 838 × 292 × 194 |
| 5.90 | 33.1 | 5893 | 535 | 6808 | 842 | 0.856 | 46.5 | 13.0 | 221 | 224 | 175.9 | 838 × 292 × 176 |
| 5.71 | 30.9 | 6234 | 610 | 7167 | 959 | 0.869 | 33.2 | 11.3 | 404 | 251 | 196.8 | 762 × 267 × 197 |
| 5.58 | 30.5 | 5387 | 514 | 6198 | 807 | 0.864 | 38.1 | 9.39 | 267 | 220 | 173.0 | 762 × 267 × 173 |
| 5.40 | 30.0 | 4470 | 411 | 5156 | 647 | 0.858 | 45.2 | 7.40 | 159 | 187 | 146.9 | 762 × 267 × 147 |
| 5.30 | 29.7 | 4018 | 362 | 4644 | 570 | 0.854 | 49.8 | 6.46 | 119 | 171 | 133.9 | 762 × 267 × 134 |
| 5.53 | 28.0 | 4916 | 518 | 5631 | 811 | 0.872 | 31.8 | 7.42 | 308 | 217 | 170.2 | 686 × 254 × 170 |
| 5.46 | 27.8 | 4374 | 455 | 5000 | 710 | 0.871 | 35.5 | 6.42 | 220 | 194 | 152.4 | 686 × 254 × 152 |
| 5.39 | 27.6 | 3987 | 409 | 4558 | 638 | 0.868 | 38.7 | 5.72 | 169 | 178 | 140.1 | 686 × 254 × 140 |
| 5.24 | 27.2 | 3481 | 346 | 3994 | 542 | 0.862 | 43.9 | 4.80 | 116 | 159 | 125.2 | 686 × 254 × 125 |
| 7.23 | 26.3 | 6589 | 1017 | 7486 | 1574 | 0.886 | 21.3 | 14.5 | 875 | 303 | 238.1 | 610 × 305 × 238 |
| 7.07 | 25.9 | 4935 | 743 | 5547 | 1144 | 0.886 | 27.7 | 10.2 | 340 | 228 | 179.0 | 610 × 305 × 179 |

*This table continues on page 237*

*This table begins on the opposite page*

*This table is completed on the opposite page*

| Designation | Mass per metre kg/m | Depth of section D mm | Width of section B mm | Thickness web t mm | Thickness flange T mm | Root radius r mm | Depth between fillets d mm | Ratios for local buckling Flange B/2T | Ratios for local buckling Web d/t | Second moment of area X–X cm⁴ | Second moment of area Y–Y cm⁴ |
|---|---|---|---|---|---|---|---|---|---|---|---|
| 610 × 305 × 149 | 149.1 | 612.4 | 304.8 | 11.8 | 19.7 | 16.5 | 540.0 | 7.74 | 45.8 | 125900 | 9308 |
| 610 × 229 × 140 | 139.9 | 617.2 | 230.2 | 13.1 | 22.1 | 12.7 | 547.6 | 5.21 | 41.8 | 111800 | 4505 |
| 610 × 229 × 125 | 125.1 | 612.2 | 229.0 | 11.9 | 19.6 | 12.7 | 547.6 | 5.84 | 46.0 | 98610 | 3932 |
| 610 × 229 × 113 | 113.0 | 607.6 | 228.2 | 11.1 | 17.3 | 12.7 | 547.6 | 6.60 | 49.3 | 87320 | 3434 |
| 610 × 229 × 101 | 101.2 | 602.6 | 227.6 | 10.5 | 14.8 | 12.7 | 547.6 | 7.69 | 52.2 | 75780 | 2915 |
| 533 × 210 × 122 | 122.0 | 544.5 | 211.9 | 12.7 | 21.3 | 12.7 | 476.5 | 4.97 | 37.5 | 76040 | 3388 |
| 533 × 210 × 109 | 109.0 | 539.5 | 210.8 | 11.6 | 18.8 | 12.7 | 476.5 | 5.61 | 41.1 | 66820 | 2943 |
| 533 × 210 × 101 | 101.0 | 536.7 | 210.0 | 10.8 | 17.4 | 12.7 | 476.5 | 6.03 | 44.1 | 61520 | 2692 |
| 533 × 210 × 92 | 92.1 | 533.1 | 209.3 | 10.1 | 15.6 | 12.7 | 476.5 | 6.71 | 47.2 | 55230 | 2389 |
| 533 × 210 × 82 | 82.2 | 528.3 | 208.8 | 9.6 | 13.2 | 12.7 | 476.5 | 7.91 | 49.6 | 47540 | 2007 |
| 457 × 191 × 98 | 98.3 | 467.2 | 192.8 | 11.4 | 19.6 | 10.2 | 407.6 | 4.92 | 35.8 | 45730 | 2347 |
| 457 × 191 × 89 | 89.3 | 463.4 | 191.9 | 10.5 | 17.7 | 10.2 | 407.6 | 5.42 | 38.8 | 41020 | 2089 |
| 457 × 191 × 82 | 82.0 | 460.0 | 191.3 | 9.9 | 16.0 | 10.2 | 407.6 | 5.98 | 41.2 | 37050 | 1871 |
| 457 × 191 × 74 | 74.3 | 457.0 | 190.4 | 9.0 | 14.5 | 10.2 | 407.6 | 6.57 | 45.3 | 33320 | 1671 |
| 457 × 191 × 67 | 67.1 | 453.4 | 189.9 | 8.5 | 12.7 | 10.2 | 407.6 | 7.48 | 48.0 | 29380 | 1452 |
| 457 × 152 × 82 | 82.1 | 465.8 | 155.3 | 10.5 | 18.9 | 10.2 | 407.6 | 4.11 | 38.8 | 36590 | 1185 |
| 457 × 152 × 74 | 74.2 | 462.0 | 154.4 | 9.6 | 17.0 | 10.2 | 407.6 | 4.54 | 42.5 | 32670 | 1047 |

*This table continues on page 238*

| Radius of gyration | | Elastic modulus | | Plastic modulus | | Buckling parameter $u$ | Torsional index $x$ | Warping constant $H\,dm^6$ | Torsional constant $J\,cm^4$ | Area $cm^2$ | Mass $kg/m$ | Designation |
|---|---|---|---|---|---|---|---|---|---|---|---|---|
| 25.7 | 7.00 | 4111 | 611 | 4594 | 937 | 0.886 | 32.7 | 8.18 | 200 | 190 | 149.1 | 610 × 305 × 149 |
| 25.0 | 5.03 | 3622 | 391 | 4142 | 611 | 0.875 | 30.6 | 3.99 | 216 | 178 | 139.9 | 610 × 229 × 140 |
| 24.9 | 4.97 | 3221 | 343 | 3676 | 535 | 0.873 | 34.1 | 3.45 | 154 | 159 | 125.1 | 610 × 229 × 125 |
| 24.6 | 4.88 | 2874 | 301 | 3281 | 469 | 0.870 | 38.0 | 2.99 | 111 | 144 | 113.0 | 610 × 229 × 113 |
| 24.2 | 4.75 | 2515 | 256 | 2881 | 400 | 0.864 | 43.1 | 2.52 | 77.0 | 129 | 101.2 | 610 × 229 × 101 |
| 22.1 | 4.67 | 2793 | 320 | 3196 | 500 | 0.877 | 27.6 | 2.32 | 178 | 155 | 122.0 | 533 × 210 × 122 |
| 21.9 | 4.60 | 2477 | 279 | 2828 | 436 | 0.875 | 30.9 | 1.99 | 126 | 139 | 109.0 | 533 × 210 × 109 |
| 21.9 | 4.57 | 2292 | 256 | 2612 | 399 | 0.874 | 33.2 | 1.81 | 101 | 129 | 101.0 | 533 × 210 × 101 |
| 21.7 | 4.51 | 2072 | 228 | 2360 | 356 | 0.872 | 36.5 | 1.60 | 75.7 | 117 | 92.1 | 533 × 210 × 92 |
| 21.3 | 4.38 | 1800 | 192 | 2059 | 300 | 0.864 | 41.6 | 1.33 | 51.5 | 105 | 82.2 | 533 × 210 × 82 |
| 19.1 | 4.33 | 1957 | 243 | 2232 | 379 | 0.881 | 25.7 | 1.18 | 121 | 125 | 98.3 | 457 × 191 × 98 |
| 19.0 | 4.29 | 1770 | 218 | 2014 | 338 | 0.880 | 28.3 | 1.04 | 90.7 | 114 | 89.3 | 457 × 191 × 89 |
| 18.8 | 4.23 | 1611 | 196 | 1831 | 304 | 0.877 | 30.9 | 0.922 | 69.2 | 104 | 82.0 | 457 × 191 × 82 |
| 18.8 | 4.20 | 1458 | 176 | 1653 | 272 | 0.877 | 33.9 | 0.818 | 51.8 | 94.6 | 74.3 | 457 × 191 × 74 |
| 18.5 | 4.12 | 1296 | 153 | 1471 | 237 | 0.872 | 37.9 | 0.705 | 37.1 | 85.5 | 67.1 | 457 × 191 × 67 |
| 18.7 | 3.37 | 1571 | 153 | 1811 | 240 | 0.873 | 27.4 | 0.519 | 89.2 | 105 | 82.1 | 457 × 152 × 82 |
| 18.6 | 3.33 | 1414 | 136 | 1627 | 213 | 0.873 | 30.1 | 0.518 | 65.9 | 94.5 | 74.2 | 457 × 152 × 74 |

*This table continues on page 239*

*This table begins on the opposite page*

*This table is completed on the opposite page*

| Designation | Mass per metre | Depth of sections | Width of sections | Thickness web | Thickness flange | Root radius | Depth between fillets | Ratios for local buckling | | Second moment of area | |
|---|---|---|---|---|---|---|---|---|---|---|---|
| | | D | B | t | T | r | d | Flange B/2T | Web d/t | X–X | Y–Y |
| | kg/m | mm | mm | mm | mm | mm | mm | | | cm⁴ | cm⁴ |
| 457 × 152 × 67 | 67.2 | 458.0 | 153.8 | 9.0 | 15.0 | 10.2 | 407.6 | 5.13 | 45.3 | 28930 | 913 |
| 457 × 152 × 60 | 59.8 | 454.6 | 152.9 | 8.1 | 13.3 | 10.2 | 407.6 | 5.75 | 50.3 | 25500 | 795 |
| 457 × 152 × 52 | 52.3 | 449.8 | 152.4 | 7.6 | 10.9 | 10.2 | 407.6 | 6.99 | 53.6 | 21370 | 645 |
| 406 × 178 × 74 | 74.2 | 412.8 | 179.5 | 9.5 | 16.0 | 10.2 | 360.4 | 5.61 | 37.9 | 27310 | 1545 |
| 406 × 178 × 67 | 67.1 | 409.4 | 178.8 | 8.8 | 14.3 | 10.2 | 360.4 | 6.25 | 41.0 | 24330 | 1365 |
| 406 × 178 × 60 | 60.1 | 406.4 | 177.9 | 7.9 | 12.8 | 10.2 | 360.4 | 6.95 | 45.6 | 21600 | 1203 |
| 406 × 178 × 54 | 54.1 | 402.6 | 177.7 | 7.7 | 10.9 | 10.2 | 360.4 | 8.15 | 46.8 | 18720 | 1021 |
| 406 × 140 × 46 | 46.0 | 403.2 | 142.2 | 6.8 | 11.2 | 10.2 | 360.4 | 6.35 | 53.0 | 15690 | 538 |
| 406 × 140 × 39 | 39.0 | 398.0 | 141.8 | 6.4 | 8.6 | 10.2 | 360.4 | 8.24 | 56.3 | 12510 | 410 |
| 356 × 171 × 67 | 67.1 | 363.4 | 173.2 | 9.1 | 15.7 | 10.2 | 311.6 | 5.52 | 34.2 | 19460 | 1362 |
| 356 × 171 × 57 | 57.0 | 358.0 | 172.2 | 8.1 | 13.0 | 10.2 | 311.6 | 6.62 | 38.5 | 16040 | 1108 |
| 356 × 171 × 51 | 51.0 | 355.0 | 171.5 | 7.4 | 11.5 | 10.2 | 311.6 | 7.46 | 42.1 | 14140 | 968 |
| 356 × 171 × 45 | 45.0 | 351.4 | 171.1 | 7.0 | 9.7 | 10.2 | 311.6 | 8.82 | 44.5 | 12070 | 811 |
| 356 × 127 × 39 | 39.1 | 353.4 | 126.0 | 6.6 | 10.7 | 10.2 | 311.6 | 5.89 | 47.2 | 10170 | 358 |
| 356 × 127 × 33 | 33.1 | 349.0 | 125.4 | 6.0 | 8.5 | 10.2 | 311.6 | 7.38 | 51.9 | 8249 | 280 |
| 305 × 165 × 54 | 54.0 | 310.4 | 166.9 | 7.9 | 13.7 | 8.9 | 265.2 | 6.09 | 33.6 | 11700 | 1063 |
| 305 × 165 × 46 | 46.1 | 306.6 | 165.7 | 6.7 | 11.8 | 8.9 | 265.2 | 7.02 | 39.6 | 9899 | 896 |
| 305 × 165 × 40 | 40.3 | 303.4 | 165.0 | 6.0 | 10.2 | 8.9 | 265.2 | 8.09 | 44.2 | 8503 | 764 |

*This table continues on page 240*

| Designation | Mass kg/m | Area cm² | Torsional constant J cm⁴ | Warping constant H dm⁶ | Torsional index x | Buckling parameter u | Plastic modulus Axis Y-Y cm³ | Plastic modulus Axis X-X cm³ | Elastic modulus Axis Y-Y cm³ | Elastic modulus Axis X-X cm³ | Radius of gyration Axis Y-Y cm | Radius of gyration Axis X-X cm |
|---|---|---|---|---|---|---|---|---|---|---|---|---|
| 457 × 152 × 67 | 67.2 | 85.6 | 47.7 | 0.448 | 33.6 | 0.869 | 187 | 1453 | 119 | 1263 | 3.27 | 18.4 |
| 457 × 152 × 60 | 59.8 | 78.2 | 33.8 | 0.387 | 37.5 | 0.868 | 163 | 1287 | 104 | 1122 | 3.23 | 18.3 |
| 457 × 152 × 52 | 52.3 | 68.6 | 21.4 | 0.311 | 43.9 | 0.859 | 133 | 1096 | 84.6 | 950 | 3.11 | 17.9 |
| 406 × 178 × 74 | 74.2 | 94.5 | 82.8 | 0.608 | 27.6 | 0.882 | 267 | 1501 | 172 | 1323 | 4.04 | 17.0 |
| 406 × 178 × 67 | 67.1 | 85.5 | 46.1 | 0.533 | 30.5 | 0.880 | 237 | 1346 | 153 | 1189 | 3.99 | 16.9 |
| 406 × 178 × 60 | 60.1 | 76.5 | 33.3 | 0.466 | 33.8 | 0.880 | 209 | 1199 | 135 | 1063 | 3.97 | 16.8 |
| 406 × 178 × 54 | 54.1 | 69.0 | 23.1 | 0.392 | 38.3 | 0.871 | 178 | 1055 | 115 | 930 | 3.85 | 16.5 |
| 406 × 140 × 46 | 46.0 | 58.6 | 19.0 | 0.207 | 38.9 | 0.871 | 118 | 888 | 75.7 | 778 | 3.03 | 16.4 |
| 406 × 140 × 39 | 39.0 | 49.7 | 10.7 | 0.155 | 47.5 | 0.858 | 90.8 | 724 | 57.8 | 629 | 2.87 | 15.9 |
| 356 × 171 × 67 | 67.1 | 85.5 | 55.7 | 0.412 | 24.4 | 0.886 | 243 | 1211 | 157 | 1071 | 3.99 | 15.1 |
| 356 × 171 × 57 | 57.0 | 72.6 | 33.4 | 0.330 | 28.8 | 0.882 | 199 | 1010 | 129 | 896 | 3.91 | 14.9 |
| 356 × 171 × 51 | 51.0 | 64.9 | 23.8 | 0.286 | 32.1 | 0.881 | 174 | 896 | 113 | 796 | 3.86 | 14.8 |
| 356 × 171 × 45 | 45.0 | 57.3 | 15.8 | 0.237 | 36.8 | 0.874 | 147 | 775 | 94.8 | 687 | 3.76 | 14.5 |
| 356 × 127 × 39 | 39.1 | 49.8 | 15.1 | 0.105 | 35.2 | 0.871 | 89.1 | 659 | 56.8 | 576 | 2.68 | 14.3 |
| 356 × 127 × 33 | 33.1 | 42.1 | 8.79 | 0.0812 | 42.2 | 0.863 | 70.3 | 543 | 44.7 | 473 | 2.58 | 14.0 |
| 305 × 165 × 54 | 54.0 | 68.8 | 34.8 | 0.234 | 23.6 | 0.889 | 196 | 846 | 127 | 754 | 3.93 | 13.0 |
| 305 × 165 × 46 | 46.1 | 58.7 | 22.2 | 0.195 | 27.1 | 0.891 | 166 | 720 | 108 | 646 | 3.90 | 13.0 |
| 305 × 165 × 40 | 40.3 | 51.3 | 14.7 | 0.164 | 31.0 | 0.889 | 142 | 623 | 92.6 | 580 | 3.86 | 12.9 |

*This table continues on page 241*

*This table begins on the opposite page*

*This table is completed on the opposite page*

| Designation | Mass per metre kg/m | Depth of sections D mm | Width of sections B mm | Thickness web t mm | Thickness flange T mm | Root radius r mm | Depth between fillets d mm | Ratios for local buckling Flange B/2T | Web d/t | Second moment of area X–X cm⁴ | Y–Y cm⁴ |
|---|---|---|---|---|---|---|---|---|---|---|---|
| 305 × 127 × 48 | 48.1 | 311.0 | 125.3 | 9.0 | 14.0 | 8.9 | 265.2 | 4.47 | 29.5 | 9575 | 461 |
| 305 × 127 × 42 | 41.9 | 307.2 | 124.3 | 8.0 | 12.1 | 8.9 | 265.2 | 5.14 | 33.2 | 8196 | 389 |
| 305 × 127 × 37 | 37.0 | 304.4 | 123.3 | 7.1 | 10.7 | 8.9 | 265.2 | 5.77 | 37.4 | 7171 | 336 |
| 305 × 102 × 33 | 32.8 | 312.7 | 102.4 | 6.6 | 10.8 | 7.6 | 275.9 | 4.74 | 41.8 | 6501 | 194 |
| 305 × 102 × 28 | 28.2 | 308.7 | 101.8 | 6.0 | 8.8 | 7.6 | 275.9 | 5.78 | 46.0 | 5366 | 155 |
| 305 × 102 × 25 | 24.8 | 305.1 | 101.6 | 5.8 | 7.0 | 7.6 | 275.9 | 7.26 | 47.6 | 4455 | 123 |
| 254 × 146 × 43 | 43.0 | 259.6 | 147.3 | 7.2 | 12.7 | 7.6 | 219.0 | 5.80 | 30.4 | 6544 | 677 |
| 254 × 146 × 37 | 37.0 | 256.0 | 146.4 | 6.3 | 10.9 | 7.6 | 219.0 | 6.72 | 34.8 | 5537 | 571 |
| 254 × 146 × 31 | 31.1 | 251.4 | 146.1 | 6.0 | 8.6 | 7.6 | 219.0 | 8.49 | 36.5 | 4413 | 448 |
| 254 × 102 × 28 | 28.3 | 260.4 | 102.2 | 6.3 | 10.0 | 7.6 | 225.2 | 5.11 | 35.7 | 4005 | 179 |
| 254 × 102 × 25 | 25.2 | 257.2 | 101.9 | 6.0 | 8.4 | 7.6 | 225.2 | 6.07 | 37.5 | 3415 | 149 |
| 254 × 102 × 22 | 22.0 | 254.0 | 101.6 | 5.7 | 6.6 | 7.6 | 225.2 | 7.47 | 39.5 | 2841 | 119 |
| 203 × 133 × 30 | 30.0 | 206.8 | 133.9 | 6.4 | 9.6 | 7.6 | 172.4 | 6.97 | 26.9 | 2896 | 385 |
| 203 × 133 × 25 | 25.1 | 203.2 | 133.2 | 5.7 | 7.8 | 7.6 | 172.4 | 8.54 | 30.2 | 2340 | 308 |
| 203 × 102 × 23 | 23.1 | 203.2 | 101.8 | 5.4 | 9.3 | 7.6 | 169.4 | 5.47 | 31.4 | 2105 | 164 |
| 178 × 102 × 19 | 19.0 | 177.8 | 101.2 | 4.8 | 7.9 | 7.6 | 146.8 | 6.41 | 30.6 | 1356 | 137 |
| 152 × 89 × 16 | 16.0 | 152.4 | 88.7 | 4.4 | 7.7 | 7.6 | 121.8 | 5.76 | 27.1 | 834 | 89.8 |
| 127 × 76 × 13 | 13.0 | 127.0 | 76.0 | 4.0 | 7.6 | 7.6 | 96.6 | 5.00 | 24.1 | 473 | 55.7 |

| Radius of gyration | | Elastic modulus | | Plastic modulus | | Buckling parameter | Torsional index | Warping constant | Torsional constant | Area | Mass | Designation |
|---|---|---|---|---|---|---|---|---|---|---|---|---|
| Axis X-X cm | Axis Y-Y cm | Axis X-X cm³ | Axis Y-Y cm³ | Axis X-X cm³ | Axis Y-Y cm³ | u | x | H dm⁶ | J cm⁴ | cm² | kg/m | |
| 12.5 | 2.74 | 616 | 73.6 | 711 | 116 | 0.873 | 23.3 | 0.102 | 31.8 | 61.2 | 48.1 | 305 × 127 × 48 |
| 12.4 | 2.70 | 534 | 62.6 | 614 | 98.4 | 0.872 | 26.5 | 0.0846 | 21.1 | 53.4 | 41.9 | 305 × 127 × 42 |
| 12.3 | 2.67 | 471 | 54.5 | 539 | 85.4 | 0.872 | 29.7 | 0.0725 | 14.8 | 47.2 | 37.0 | 305 × 127 × 37 |
| 12.5 | 2.15 | 416 | 37.9 | 481 | 60.0 | 0.866 | 31.6 | 0.0442 | 12.2 | 41.8 | 32.8 | 305 × 102 × 33 |
| 12.2 | 2.08 | 348 | 30.5 | 403 | 48.5 | 0.859 | 37.4 | 0.0349 | 7.40 | 35.9 | 28.2 | 305 × 102 × 28 |
| 11.9 | 1.97 | 292 | 24.2 | 342 | 38.8 | 0.846 | 43.4 | 0.0273 | 4.77 | 31.6 | 24.8 | 305 × 102 × 25 |
| 10.9 | 3.52 | 504 | 92.0 | 566 | 141 | 0.891 | 21.2 | 0.103 | 23.9 | 54.8 | 43.0 | 254 × 146 × 43 |
| 10.8 | 3.48 | 433 | 78.0 | 483 | 119 | 0.890 | 24.3 | 0.0857 | 15.3 | 47.2 | 37.0 | 254 × 146 × 37 |
| 10.5 | 3.36 | 351 | 61.3 | 393 | 94.1 | 0.880 | 29.6 | 0.0660 | 8.55 | 39.7 | 31.1 | 254 × 146 × 31 |
| 10.5 | 2.22 | 308 | 34.9 | 353 | 54.8 | 0.874 | 27.5 | 0.0280 | 9.57 | 36.1 | 28.3 | 254 × 102 × 28 |
| 10.3 | 2.15 | 266 | 29.2 | 306 | 46.0 | 0.866 | 31.5 | 0.0230 | 6.42 | 32.0 | 25.2 | 254 × 102 × 25 |
| 10.1 | 2.06 | 224 | 23.5 | 259 | 37.3 | 0.856 | 36.4 | 0.0182 | 4.15 | 28.0 | 22.0 | 254 × 102 × 22 |
| 8.71 | 3.17 | 280 | 57.5 | 314 | 88.2 | 0.881 | 21.5 | 0.0374 | 10.3 | 38.2 | 30.0 | 203 × 133 × 30 |
| 8.56 | 3.10 | 230 | 46.2 | 258 | 70.9 | 0.877 | 25.6 | 0.0294 | 5.96 | 32.0 | 25.1 | 203 × 133 × 25 |
| 8.46 | 2.36 | 207 | 32.2 | 234 | 49.8 | 0.888 | 22.5 | 0.0154 | 7.02 | 29.4 | 23.1 | 203 × 102 × 23 |
| 7.48 | 2.37 | 153 | 27.0 | 171 | 41.6 | 0.888 | 22.6 | 0.00987 | 4.41 | 24.3 | 19.0 | 178 × 102 × 19 |
| 6.41 | 2.10 | 109 | 20.2 | 123 | 31.2 | 0.890 | 19.6 | 0.00470 | 3.56 | 20.3 | 16.0 | 152 × 89 × 16 |
| 5.35 | 1.84 | 74.6 | 14.7 | 84.2 | 22.6 | 0.898 | 16.3 | 0.00199 | 2.85 | 16.5 | 13.0 | 127 × 76 × 13 |

*This table begins on the opposite page*

# Appendix C

## Universal column section properties

*The following four pages form one large table. The depth of the table can be seen in the even pages 244 and 246. The width of the table can be seen in facing pairs of even and odd pages; thus pages 244 and 245 form the whole width and about half of the whole table.*

*This table is completed on the opposite page*

| Designation | Mass per metre kg/m | Depth of section D mm | Width of section B mm | Thickness web t mm | Thickness flange T mm | Root radius r mm | Depth between fillets d mm | Ratio for local buckling Flange B/2T | Ratio for local buckling Web d/t | Second moment of area X–X cm⁴ | Second moment of area Y–Y cm⁴ |
|---|---|---|---|---|---|---|---|---|---|---|---|
| 356 × 406 × 634 | 633.9 | 474.6 | 424.0 | 47.6 | 77.0 | 15.2 | 290.2 | 2.75 | 6.10 | 274800 | 98130 |
| 356 × 406 × 551 | 551.0 | 455.6 | 416.5 | 42.1 | 67.5 | 15.2 | 290.2 | 3.10 | 6.89 | 226900 | 82670 |
| 356 × 406 × 467 | 467.0 | 436.6 | 412.2 | 35.8 | 58.0 | 15.2 | 290.2 | 3.55 | 8.11 | 183000 | 67830 |
| 356 × 406 × 393 | 393.0 | 419.0 | 407.0 | 30.6 | 49.2 | 15.2 | 290.2 | 4.14 | 9.46 | 146600 | 55370 |
| 356 × 406 × 340 | 339.9 | 406.4 | 403.0 | 26.6 | 42.9 | 15.2 | 290.2 | 4.70 | 10.9 | 122500 | 46850 |
| 356 × 406 × 287 | 287.1 | 393.6 | 399.0 | 22.6 | 36.5 | 15.2 | 290.2 | 5.47 | 12.6 | 99880 | 38680 |
| 356 × 406 × 235 | 235.1 | 381.0 | 394.8 | 18.4 | 30.2 | 15.2 | 290.2 | 6.54 | 15.8 | 79080 | 30990 |
| 356 × 368 × 202 | 201.9 | 374.6 | 374.4 | 16.5 | 27.0 | 15.2 | 290.2 | 6.94 | 17.6 | 66260 | 23690 |
| 356 × 368 × 177 | 177.0 | 368.2 | 372.6 | 14.4 | 23.8 | 15.2 | 290.2 | 7.83 | 20.2 | 57120 | 20530 |
| 356 × 368 × 153 | 152.9 | 362.0 | 370.5 | 12.3 | 20.7 | 15.2 | 290.2 | 8.95 | 23.6 | 48590 | 17550 |
| 356 × 368 × 129 | 129.0 | 355.6 | 368.6 | 10.4 | 17.5 | 15.2 | 290.2 | 10.50 | 27.9 | 40250 | 14610 |
| 305 × 305 × 283 | 282.9 | 365.3 | 322.2 | 26.8 | 44.1 | 15.2 | 246.7 | 3.65 | 9.21 | 78870 | 24630 |
| 305 × 305 × 240 | 240.0 | 352.5 | 318.4 | 23.0 | 37.7 | 15.2 | 246.7 | 4.22 | 10.7 | 64200 | 20310 |
| 305 × 305 × 198 | 198.1 | 339.9 | 314.5 | 19.1 | 31.4 | 15.2 | 246.7 | 5.01 | 12.9 | 50900 | 16300 |
| 305 × 305 × 158 | 158.1 | 327.1 | 311.2 | 15.8 | 25.0 | 15.2 | 246.7 | 6.22 | 15.6 | 38750 | 12570 |
| 305 × 305 × 137 | 136.9 | 320.5 | 309.2 | 13.8 | 21.7 | 15.2 | 246.7 | 7.12 | 17.9 | 32810 | 10700 |
| 305 × 305 × 118 | 117.9 | 314.5 | 307.4 | 12.0 | 18.7 | 15.2 | 246.7 | 8.22 | 20.6 | 27670 | 9059 |
| 305 × 305 × 97 | 96.9 | 307.9 | 305.3 | 9.9 | 15.4 | 15.2 | 246.7 | 9.91 | 24.9 | 22250 | 7308 |

*This table continues on page 246*

| Radius of gyration | | Elastic modulus | | Plastic modulus | | Buckling parameter | Torsional index | Warping constant | Torsional constant | Area | Mass | Designation |
|---|---|---|---|---|---|---|---|---|---|---|---|---|
| Axis X-X cm | Axis Y-Y cm | Axis X-X cm³ | Axis Y-Y cm³ | Axis X-X cm³ | Axis Y-Y cm³ | u | x | H dm⁶ | J cm⁴ | A cm² | kg/m | |
| 18.4 | 11.0 | 11580 | 4629 | 14240 | 7108 | 0.843 | 5.46 | 38.8 | 13720 | 808 | 633.9 | 356 × 406 × 634 |
| 18.0 | 10.9 | 9962 | 3951 | 12080 | 6058 | 0.841 | 6.05 | 31.1 | 9240 | 702 | 551.0 | 356 × 406 × 551 |
| 17.5 | 10.7 | 8383 | 3291 | 10000 | 5034 | 0.839 | 6.86 | 24.3 | 5809 | 595 | 467.0 | 356 × 406 × 467 |
| 17.1 | 10.5 | 6998 | 2721 | 8222 | 4154 | 0.837 | 7.86 | 18.9 | 3545 | 501 | 393.0 | 356 × 406 × 393 |
| 16.8 | 10.4 | 6031 | 2325 | 6999 | 3544 | 0.836 | 8.85 | 15.5 | 2343 | 433 | 339.9 | 356 × 406 × 340 |
| 16.5 | 10.3 | 5075 | 1939 | 5812 | 2949 | 0.835 | 10.2 | 12.3 | 1441 | 366 | 287.1 | 356 × 406 × 287 |
| 16.3 | 10.2 | 4151 | 1570 | 4687 | 2363 | 0.834 | 12.1 | 9.54 | 812 | 299 | 235.1 | 356 × 406 × 235 |
| 16.1 | 9.60 | 3538 | 1264 | 3972 | 1920 | 0.844 | 13.4 | 7.16 | 558 | 257 | 201.9 | 356 × 368 × 202 |
| 15.9 | 9.54 | 3103 | 1102 | 3455 | 1671 | 0.844 | 15.0 | 6.09 | 381 | 226 | 177.0 | 356 × 368 × 177 |
| 15.8 | 9.49 | 2664 | 948 | 2965 | 1435 | 0.844 | 17.0 | 5.11 | 251 | 195 | 152.9 | 356 × 368 × 153 |
| 15.6 | 9.43 | 2264 | 793 | 2479 | 1199 | 0.844 | 19.9 | 4.18 | 153 | 164 | 129.0 | 356 × 368 × 129 |
| 14.8 | 8.27 | 4318 | 1529 | 5105 | 2342 | 0.855 | 7.65 | 6.35 | 2034 | 360 | 282.9 | 305 × 305 × 283 |
| 14.5 | 8.15 | 3643 | 1276 | 4247 | 1951 | 0.854 | 8.74 | 5.03 | 1271 | 306 | 240.0 | 305 × 305 × 240 |
| 14.2 | 8.04 | 2995 | 1037 | 3440 | 1581 | 0.854 | 10.2 | 3.88 | 734 | 252 | 198.1 | 305 × 305 × 198 |
| 13.9 | 7.90 | 2369 | 808 | 2680 | 1230 | 0.851 | 12.5 | 2.87 | 378 | 201 | 158.1 | 305 × 305 × 158 |
| 13.7 | 7.83 | 2048 | 692 | 2297 | 1053 | 0.851 | 14.2 | 2.39 | 249 | 174 | 136.9 | 305 × 305 × 137 |
| 13.6 | 7.77 | 1760 | 589 | 1958 | 895 | 0.850 | 16.2 | 1.98 | 161 | 150 | 117.9 | 305 × 305 × 118 |
| 13.4 | 7.69 | 1445 | 479 | 1592 | 726 | 0.850 | 19.3 | 1.56 | 91.2 | 123 | 96.9 | 305 × 305 × 97 |

*This table continues on page 247*

*This table begins on the opposite page*

*This table is completed on the opposite page*

| Designation | Mass per metre kg/m | Depth of section D mm | Width of section B mm | Thickness web t mm | Thickness flange T mm | Root radius r mm | Depth between fillets d mm | Ratio for local buckling Flange B/2T | Web d/t | Second moment of area X–X cm⁴ | Y–Y cm⁴ |
|---|---|---|---|---|---|---|---|---|---|---|---|
| 254 × 254 × 167 | 167.1 | 289.1 | 265.2 | 19.2 | 31.7 | 12.7 | 200.3 | 4.18 | 10.4 | 30000 | 9870 |
| 254 × 254 × 132 | 132.0 | 276.3 | 261.3 | 15.3 | 25.3 | 12.7 | 200.3 | 5.16 | 13.1 | 22530 | 7531 |
| 254 × 254 × 107 | 107.1 | 266.7 | 258.8 | 12.8 | 20.5 | 12.7 | 200.3 | 6.31 | 15.6 | 17510 | 5928 |
| 254 × 254 × 89 | 88.9 | 260.3 | 256.3 | 10.3 | 17.3 | 12.7 | 200.3 | 7.41 | 19.4 | 14270 | 4857 |
| 254 × 254 × 73 | 73.1 | 254.1 | 254.6 | 8.6 | 14.2 | 12.7 | 200.3 | 8.96 | 23.3 | 11410 | 3908 |
| 203 × 203 × 86 | 86.1 | 222.2 | 209.1 | 12.7 | 20.5 | 10.2 | 160.8 | 5.10 | 12.7 | 9449 | 3127 |
| 203 × 203 × 71 | 71.0 | 215.8 | 206.4 | 10.0 | 17.3 | 10.2 | 160.8 | 5.97 | 16.1 | 7618 | 2537 |
| 203 × 203 × 60 | 60.0 | 209.6 | 205.8 | 9.4 | 14.2 | 10.2 | 160.8 | 7.25 | 17.1 | 6125 | 2065 |
| 203 × 203 × 52 | 52.0 | 206.2 | 204.3 | 7.9 | 12.5 | 10.2 | 160.8 | 8.17 | 20.4 | 5259 | 1778 |
| 203 × 203 × 46 | 46.1 | 203.2 | 203.6 | 7.2 | 11.0 | 10.2 | 160.8 | 9.25 | 22.3 | 4568 | 1548 |
| 152 × 152 × 37 | 37.0 | 161.8 | 154.4 | 8.0 | 11.5 | 7.6 | 123.6 | 6.71 | 15.4 | 2210 | 706 |
| 152 × 152 × 30 | 30.0 | 157.6 | 152.9 | 6.5 | 9.4 | 7.6 | 123.6 | 8.13 | 19.0 | 1748 | 560 |
| 152 × 152 × 23 | 23.0 | 152.4 | 152.2 | 5.8 | 6.8 | 7.6 | 123.6 | 11.20 | 21.3 | 1250 | 400 |

| Radius of gyration | | Elastic modulus | | Plastic modulus | | Buckling parameter | Torsional index | Warping constant | Torsional constant | Area | Mass | Designation |
|---|---|---|---|---|---|---|---|---|---|---|---|---|
| Axis X–X cm | Axis Y–Y cm | Axis X–X cm³ | Axis Y–Y cm³ | Axis X–X cm³ | Axis Y–Y cm³ | $u$ | $x$ | $H$ dm⁶ | $J$ cm⁴ | $A$ cm² | kg/m | |
| 11.9 | 6.81 | 2075 | 744 | 2424 | 1137 | 0.851 | 8.49 | 1.63 | 626 | 213 | 167.1 | 254 × 254 × 167 |
| 11.6 | 6.69 | 1631 | 576 | 1869 | 878 | 0.850 | 10.3 | 1.19 | 319 | 168 | 132.0 | 254 × 254 × 132 |
| 11.3 | 6.59 | 1313 | 458 | 1484 | 697 | 0.848 | 12.4 | 0.898 | 172 | 136 | 107.1 | 254 × 254 × 107 |
| 11.2 | 6.55 | 1096 | 379 | 1224 | 575 | 0.850 | 14.5 | 0.717 | 102 | 113 | 88.9 | 254 × 254 × 89 |
| 11.1 | 6.48 | 898 | 307 | 992 | 465 | 0.849 | 17.3 | 0.562 | 57.6 | 93.1 | 73.1 | 254 × 254 × 73 |
| 9.28 | 5.34 | 850 | 299 | 977 | 456 | 0.850 | 10.2 | 0.318 | 137 | 110 | 86.1 | 203 × 203 × 86 |
| 9.18 | 5.30 | 706 | 246 | 799 | 374 | 0.853 | 11.9 | 0.250 | 80.2 | 90.4 | 71.0 | 203 × 203 × 71 |
| 8.96 | 5.20 | 584 | 201 | 656 | 305 | 0.846 | 14.1 | 0.197 | 47.2 | 76.4 | 60.0 | 203 × 203 × 60 |
| 8.91 | 5.18 | 510 | 174 | 567 | 264 | 0.848 | 15.8 | 0.167 | 31.8 | 66.3 | 52.0 | 203 × 203 × 52 |
| 8.82 | 5.13 | 450 | 152 | 497 | 231 | 0.847 | 17.7 | 0.143 | 22.2 | 58.7 | 46.1 | 203 × 203 × 46 |
| 6.85 | 3.87 | 273 | 91.5 | 309 | 140 | 0.848 | 13.3 | 0.0399 | 19.2 | 47.1 | 37.0 | 152 × 152 × 37 |
| 6.76 | 3.83 | 222 | 73.3 | 248 | 112 | 0.849 | 16.0 | 0.0308 | 10.5 | 38.3 | 30.0 | 152 × 152 × 30 |
| 6.54 | 3.70 | 164 | 52.6 | 182 | 80.2 | 0.840 | 20.7 | 0.0212 | 4.63 | 29.2 | 23.0 | 152 × 152 × 23 |

*This table begins on the opposite page*

# Appendix D

**Equal angles section properties**

**Unequal angles section properties**

*The following four pages form two large tables. The first table extends over pages 250 and 251, the second over 253 and 254*

# Equal angles section properties

| Designation | Mass | Root radius $r_1$ | Radius toe $r_2$ | Area | Distance of centre of gravity $c_x$ & $c_y$ | Second moment of area Axis $X$-$X$ & $Y$-$Y$ | Axis $U$-$U$ | Axis $V$-$V$ | Radius of gyration Axis $X$-$X$ & $Y$-$Y$ | Axis $U$-$U$ | Axis $V$-$V$ | Elastic modulus $X$-$X$ & $Y$-$Y$ | Designation |
|---|---|---|---|---|---|---|---|---|---|---|---|---|---|
| | kg/m | mm | mm | cm² | cm | cm⁴ | cm⁴ | cm⁴ | cm | cm | cm | cm³ | |
| 200 × 200 × 24 | 71.1 | 18.0 | 9.0 | 90.6 | 5.84 | 3330 | 5280 | 1380 | 6.06 | 7.64 | 3.90 | 235.0 | 200 × 200 × 24 |
| 200 × 200 × 20 | 59.9 | 18.0 | 9.0 | 76.3 | 5.68 | 2850 | 4530 | 1170 | 6.11 | 7.70 | 3.92 | 199.0 | 200 × 200 × 20 |
| 200 × 200 × 18 | 54.3 | 18.0 | 9.0 | 69.1 | 5.60 | 2600 | 4150 | 1050 | 6.13 | 7.75 | 3.90 | 181.0 | 200 × 200 × 18 |
| 200 × 200 × 16 | 48.5 | 18.0 | 9.0 | 61.8 | 5.52 | 2340 | 3720 | 960 | 6.16 | 7.76 | 3.94 | 162.0 | 200 × 200 × 16 |
| 150 × 150 × 18 | 40.1 | 16.0 | 8.0 | 51.0 | 4.37 | 1050 | 1670 | 435 | 4.54 | 5.71 | 2.92 | 98.7 | 150 × 150 × 18 |
| 150 × 150 × 15 | 33.8 | 16.0 | 8.0 | 43.0 | 4.25 | 898 | 1430 | 370 | 4.57 | 5.76 | 2.93 | 83.5 | 150 × 150 × 15 |
| 150 × 150 × 12 | 27.3 | 16.0 | 8.0 | 34.8 | 4.12 | 737 | 1170 | 303 | 4.60 | 5.80 | 2.95 | 67.7 | 150 × 150 × 12 |
| 150 × 150 × 10 | 23.0 | 16.0 | 8.0 | 29.3 | 4.03 | 624 | 990 | 258 | 4.62 | 5.62 | 2.97 | 56.9 | 150 × 150 × 10 |
| 120 × 120 × 15 | 26.6 | 13.0 | 6.5 | 33.9 | 3.51 | 445 | 705 | 185 | 3.62 | 4.56 | 2.33 | 52.4 | 120 × 120 × 15 |
| 120 × 120 × 12 | 21.6 | 13.0 | 6.5 | 27.5 | 3.40 | 368 | 584 | 152 | 3.66 | 4.60 | 2.35 | 42.7 | 120 × 120 × 12 |
| 120 × 120 × 10 | 18.2 | 13.0 | 6.5 | 23.2 | 3.31 | 313 | 497 | 129 | 3.67 | 4.63 | 2.36 | 36.0 | 120 × 120 × 10 |
| 120 × 120 × 8 | 14.7 | 13.0 | 6.5 | 18.7 | 3.23 | 255 | 405 | 105 | 3.69 | 4.65 | 2.37 | 29.1 | 120 × 120 × 8 |

| | kg/m | $r_1$ mm | $r_2$ mm | cm² | $c_x$ & $c_y$ cm | Axis X–X & Y–Y cm⁴ | Axis U–U cm⁴ | Axis V–V cm⁴ | Axis X–X & Y–Y cm | Axis U–U cm | Axis V–V cm | X–X & Y–Y cm³ | |
|---|---|---|---|---|---|---|---|---|---|---|---|---|---|
| 100 × 100 × 15 | 21.9 | 12.0 | 6.0 | 27.9 | 3.02 | 249 | 393 | 104 | 2.98 | 3.75 | 1.93 | 35.6 | 100 × 100 × 15 |
| 100 × 100 × 12 | 17.8 | 12.0 | 6.0 | 22.7 | 2.90 | 207 | 328 | 85.7 | 3.02 | 3.80 | 1.94 | 29.1 | 100 × 100 × 12 |
| 100 × 100 × 10 | 15.0 | 12.0 | 6.0 | 19.2 | 2.62 | 177 | 280 | 73.0 | 3.04 | 3.83 | 1.95 | 24.6 | 100 × 100 × 10 |
| 100 × 100 × 8 | 12.2 | 12.0 | 6.0 | 15.5 | 2.74 | 145 | 230 | 59.9 | 3.06 | 3.85 | 1.96 | 19.9 | 100 × 100 × 8 |
| 90 × 90 × 12 | 15.9 | 11.0 | 5.5 | 20.3 | 2.66 | 148 | 234 | 61.7 | 2.70 | 3.40 | 1.74 | 23.3 | 90 × 90 × 12 |
| 90 × 90 × 10 | 13.4 | 11.0 | 5.5 | 17.1 | 2.58 | 127 | 201 | 52.6 | 2.72 | 3.42 | 1.75 | 19.8 | 90 × 90 × 10 |
| 90 × 90 × 8 | 10.9 | 11.0 | 5.5 | 13.9 | 2.50 | 104 | 166 | 43.1 | 2.74 | 3.45 | 1.76 | 16.1 | 90 × 90 × 8 |
| 90 × 90 × 7 | 9.6 | 11.0 | 5.5 | 12.2 | 2.45 | 92.5 | 147 | 38.3 | 2.75 | 3.46 | 1.77 | 14.1 | 90 × 90 × 7 |

## Unequal angles section properties

| Designation | Mass kg/m | Radius root $r_1$ mm | Radius toe $r_2$ mm | Area cm² | Distance of centre of gravity | | Second moment of area | | | | Radius of gyration | | | | Elastic modulus | | Designation |
|---|---|---|---|---|---|---|---|---|---|---|---|---|---|---|---|---|---|
| | | | | | $C_x$ mm | $C_y$ mm | Axis X–X cm⁴ | Axis Y–Y cm⁴ | Axis U–U cm⁴ | Axis V–V cm⁴ | Axis X–X cm | Axis Y–Y cm | Axis U–U cm | Axis V–V cm | Axis X–X cm³ | Axis Y–Y cm³ | |
| 200 × 150 × 18 | 47.1 | 15.0 | 7.5 | 60.0 | 6.33 | 3.85 | 2376 | 1146 | 2904 | 618 | 6.29 | 4.37 | 6.96 | 3.21 | 174 | 103 | 200 × 150 × 18 |
| 200 × 150 × 15 | 39.6 | 15.0 | 7.5 | 50.5 | 6.21 | 3.73 | 2022 | 979 | 2476 | 526 | 6.33 | 4.40 | 7.00 | 3.23 | 147 | 86.9 | 200 × 150 × 15 |
| 200 × 150 × 12 | 32.0 | 15.0 | 7.5 | 40.8 | 6.08 | 3.61 | 1650 | 803 | 2030 | 430 | 6.36 | 4.44 | 7.04 | 3.25 | 119 | 70.5 | 200 × 150 × 12 |
| 200 × 100 × 15 | 33.75 | 15.0 | 7.5 | 43.0 | 7.16 | 2.22 | 1758 | 299 | 1864 | 193 | 6.40 | 2.64 | 6.59 | 2.12 | 137 | 38.5 | 200 × 100 × 15 |
| 200 × 100 × 12 | 27.3 | 15.0 | 7.5 | 34.8 | 7.03 | 2.10 | 1440 | 247 | 1530 | 159 | 8.43 | 2.67 | 6.63 | 2.14 | 111 | 31.3 | 200 × 100 × 12 |
| 200 × 100 × 10 | 23.0 | 15.0 | 7.5 | 29.2 | 6.93 | 2.01 | 1220 | 210 | 1290 | 135 | 6.46 | 2.68 | 6.65 | 2.15 | 93.2 | 26.3 | 200 × 100 × 10 |
| 150 × 90 × 15 | 26.6 | 12.0 | 6.0 | 26.6 | 5.21 | 2.23 | 761 | 205 | 841 | 126 | 4.74 | 2.46 | 4.96 | 1.93 | 77.7 | 30.4 | 150 × 90 × 15 |
| 150 × 90 × 12 | 21.6 | 12.0 | 6.0 | 27.5 | 5.08 | 2.12 | 627 | 171 | 694 | 104 | 4.77 | 2.49 | 5.02 | 1.94 | 63.3 | 24.8 | 150 × 90 × 12 |
| 150 × 90 × 10 | 18.2 | 12.0 | 6.0 | 23.2 | 5.00 | 2.04 | 533 | 146 | 591 | 88.3 | 4.80 | 2.51 | 5.05 | 1.95 | 53.3 | 21.0 | 150 × 90 × 10 |
| 150 × 75 × 15 | 24.8 | 12.0 | 6.0 | 31.7 | 5.52 | 1.81 | 713 | 119 | 753 | 78.6 | 4.75 | 1.94 | 4.86 | 1.58 | 75.2 | 21.0 | 150 × 75 × 15 |
| 150 × 75 × 12 | 20.2 | 12.0 | 6.0 | 25.7 | 5.40 | 1.69 | 588 | 99.6 | 623 | 64.7 | 4.78 | 1.97 | 4.92 | 1.59 | 61.3 | 17.1 | 150 × 75 × 12 |
| 150 × 75 × 10 | 17.0 | 12.0 | 6.0 | 21.7 | 5.31 | 1.61 | 501 | 85.6 | 531 | 55.1 | 4.81 | 1.99 | 4.95 | 1.60 | 51.6 | 14.5 | 150 × 75 × 10 |

| | kg/m | $r_1$ mm | $r_2$ mm | $cm^2$ | $C_x$ mm | $C_y$ mm | Axis X–X $cm^4$ | Axis Y–Y $cm^4$ | Axis U–U $cm^4$ | Axis V–V $cm^4$ | Axis X–X cm | Axis Y–Y cm | Axis U–U cm | Axis V–V cm | Axis X–X $cm^3$ | Axis Y–Y $cm^3$ | |
|---|---|---|---|---|---|---|---|---|---|---|---|---|---|---|---|---|---|
| 125 × 75 × 12 | 17.8 | 11.0 | 5.5 | 22.7 | 4.31 | 1.84 | 354 | 95.5 | 391 | 58.5 | 3.95 | 2.05 | 4.15 | 1.61 | 43.2 | 16.9 | 125 × 75 × 12 |
| 125 × 75 × 10 | 15.0 | 11.0 | 5.5 | 19.1 | 4.23 | 1.76 | 302 | 82.1 | 334 | 49.9 | 3.97 | 2.07 | 4.18 | 1.61 | 36.5 | 14.3 | 125 × 75 × 10 |
| 125 × 75 × 8 | 12.2 | 11.0 | 5.5 | 15.5 | 4.14 | 1.68 | 247 | 67.6 | 274 | 40.9 | 4.00 | 2.09 | 4.21 | 1.63 | 29.6 | 11.6 | 125 × 75 × 8 |
| 100 × 75 × 12 | 15.4 | 10.0 | 5.0 | 19.7 | 3.27 | 2.03 | 189 | 90.2 | 230 | 49.5 | 3.10 | 2.14 | 3.42 | 1.59 | 28.0 | 16.5 | 100 × 75 × 12 |
| 100 × 75 × 10 | 13.0 | 10.0 | 5.0 | 16.6 | 3.19 | 1.95 | 162 | 77.6 | 197 | 42.2 | 3.12 | 2.16 | 3.45 | 1.59 | 23.8 | 14.0 | 100 × 75 × 10 |
| 100 × 75 × 8 | 10.6 | 10.0 | 5.0 | 13.5 | 3.10 | 1.87 | 133 | 64.1 | 162 | 34.6 | 3.14 | 2.18 | 3.47 | 1.60 | 19.3 | 11.4 | 100 × 75 × 8 |
| 100 × 65 × 10 | 12.3 | 10.0 | 5.0 | 15.6 | 3.36 | 1.63 | 154 | 51.0 | 175 | 30.1 | 3.14 | 1.81 | 3.35 | 1.39 | 23.2 | 10.5 | 100 × 65 × 10 |
| 100 × 65 × 8 | 9.94 | 10.0 | 5.0 | 12.7 | 3.27 | 1.55 | 127 | 42.2 | 144 | 24.8 | 3.16 | 1.83 | 3.37 | 1.40 | 18.9 | 8.54 | 100 × 65 × 8 |
| 100 × 65 × 7 | 8.77 | 10.0 | 5.0 | 11.2 | 3.23 | 1.51 | 113 | 37.6 | 128 | 22.0 | 3.17 | 1.83 | 3.39 | 1.40 | 16.6 | 7.53 | 100 × 65 × 7 |

# Appendix E

## Alternative form of purlins

The use of cold steel sections has been steadily increasing over the last few years, particularly in industrial and agricultural buildings.

There are many shapes which can be used to advantage for purlins but those most used are ZED and SIGMA sections (see Fig. E.1). These range from about 130 mm to 300 mm in depth and from 3 mm to 5 mm in thickness, and are suitable for continuous spans of up to 10 m or more. These lighter purlins are usually made from galvanised steel strip.

The advantage of these purlins is that they have a high moment of resistance with minimum use of material and large spans are economical. For the same section modulus, a cold-rolled purlin is deeper and lighter than the conventional hot-rolled section. The profiles of these purlins can also have their shear centre within the section and are therefore less liable to twist than channel or angle sections. However, at the time of writing the price per tonne of cold-formed steel sections is generally higher than hot-rolled sections and there are as yet no 'standard' sections as such. Each manufacturer markets his own sections, but the major companies concerned have loading tables based on a considerable number of loading tests.

If cold-formed purlins are adopted, the spacing of the main building frames is usually increased, but the maker's recommendations should be consulted regarding the loading and deflection to be followed.

For spans over 4.5 m, anti-sag bars form an integral part of the roofing system and fulfil important functions in stabilising the purlins during laying and fastening of the sheeting. There is some controversy as to how these anti-sag bars should be fitted. It would depend on the roof slope and the direction of loading. At low slopes, the Z, which always points 'up' the slope, twists 'forwards' and therefore should be restrained 'top to bottom', as in Fig. E.2(c). At slopes higher than about 10°, the Z twists 'backwards' so that better restraint is provided if the anti-sag bars are fitted 'bottom to top' as in Fig. E.2(b). If the wind uplift loading is critical in design, it may be necessary to modify the procedure to provide restraint to the lower (compression) flange.

BS 5950: Part 5 gives empirical rules for the design of purlins, up to a span of 8 m, which are in many ways similar to those for angle purlins in BS 5950: Part 1. It also recommends that where a purlin span exceeds 4.5 m, additional support should be provided by means of one anti-sag bar, so that the laterally unsupported length does not exceed 3.8 m. When a purlin span exceeds 7.6 m two anti-sag bars must be provided.

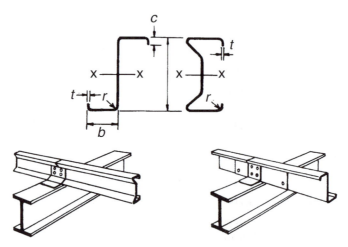

*Fig. E.1*

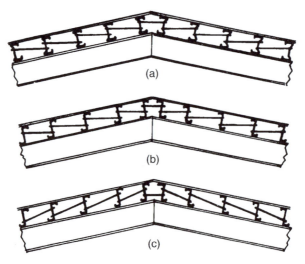

*Fig. E.2*

# Bibliography

Baker, J.F., Horne, M.R. and Heyman, J. (1956) *The Steel Skeleton*, Cambridge University Press.

Cowan, H.J. (1979) *Architectural Structures*, Elsevier.

Davies, J.M. and Brown, B.H. (1996) *Plastic Design to BS 5950*, Blackwell Scientific Publications.

Hart, F., Henn, W. and Sontag, H. (1985) *Multi-storey Buildings in Steel*, BSP Professional Books, Oxford.

Heyman, J. (1969) *Plastic Design of Frames Vol. 1*, Cambridge University Press.

Horne, M.R. (1979) *Plastic Theory of Structures*, 2nd edn., Pergamon Press.

Horne, M.R. and Morris, L. J. (1981) *Plastic Design of Low Rise Frames*, Granada.

Joannides, F. and Weller, A. (1987) *Structural Steelwork (Elementary Design to BS 5950)*, Parthenon Press (revised 1990).

*Steel Designer's Manual*. Steel Construction Institute.

# Index